Conversations with the Wise Aunt

Other Books by
Dennis E. Coates, Ph.D.

Conversations with the Wise Uncle (2012)

Adult Discussion Guides

Learning from the Wise Aunt (2012)

Learning from the Wise Uncle (2012)

Praise for
Conversations with the Wise Aunt

"I wish that I would have had this book while growing up and surviving my youth." – Karen Scherrer, retired middle school principal and youth program director

"Must read for parents, teens, and those around them." – J. Breeden, Peace Corps volunteer and former high school teacher

"It's loaded with the common sense, non-lecturing conversations that provoke thought." – Christine Johnson, President, ALD, Inc.

"Having a guide that lays out in easy-to-read terms and compelling scenarios the secrets to becoming a successful person and adult is an invaluable tool. That's what this book does." - J. Webb, retired nurse and mother of three

"This book is a fast read and is full of practical wisdom any parent can use to help prepare their daughter to be a success and responsible contributor to society." – Mike Capuzzi, direct marketing expert, business owner and father of two daughters

Conversations with the Wise Aunt

The Secret to Being Strong as a Teenager and Preparing for Success as an Adult

Dennis E. Coates, Ph.D.
Kathleen Scott

First Summit Publishing

Printed in the United States of America
First Summit Publishing
P.O. Box 1655
Newport News, VA 23601
757-873-3700

Cover photograph: Paul Kline, from
istockphoto.com
Cover design and interior composition: Paula
Schlauch
Sketches: Dennis E. Coates
Library of Congress Cataloguing-in-Publication
Data is available.

ISBN - 978-0-9850156-2-6

It's a huge blessing for a teen girl to know adults who will give her a "heads-up" about life.

We've written this book to help make that happen.

CONTENTS

The Heads-Up Talk

The idea for this book was inspired by a story Denny's best friend told him.

When his friend was 12, his uncle took him out for breakfast. In addition to potatoes and eggs, they shared a long talk. His uncle was relaxed and fun to be with, not at all like his dad, who was stern, demanding and hard to talk to.

In a friendly, casual way, his uncle talked about what the boy could expect during his teen years. He described the physical changes that were about to happen to him as he matured into an adult. He talked about peer pressure, risk-taking behavior and the consequences of sex, drugs and alcohol.

At the end of the talk his uncle said, "Now I want you to promise me something. When your friends want you to go along with them and something inside you doesn't feel right, I want you to stop and think about what could happen. I want you to remember the things we talked about. Will you do that?"

Denny's friend told him that this talk with his uncle was the most important conversation of his life, that it helped him steer clear of all kinds of trouble during his teen years. Not that he was a perfect kid, whatever that is. But most of the time when he was tempted to do something he knew he shouldn't, and usually it was something fun or exciting, he remembered what his uncle told him. He said having an uncle who leveled with him about the consequences of bad decisions was the luckiest thing that ever happened to him.

Many adults don't feel comfortable talking to kids about these things. Why? Because there's so much ground to cover, and they know they're not experts. Besides, times have changed, and they remember their own teen years as a confusing time of life, a mixed bag of issues, anxiety and fun. So even caring adults may not have the confidence to say the right things. We've talked to quite a few people about their teen experiences, and Denny's friend is the only person we've ever met who had anything like a "wise uncle" conversation.

His friend's story caused Denny to reflect on his own teen years. No one ever sat him down and explained things to him. His dad was always busy with work, and there were times when he was away from home a lot. His mom had her hands full taking care of his younger brothers and sisters.

During junior high and high school, a few adults took an interest in him—a scoutmaster, a wrestling coach, an English teacher, and an elder in his church. Later in life he was lucky to have a few colleagues and bosses who gave him advice.

The problem was, he didn't always get the coaching when he needed it, and there were huge gaps that he had to fill in on his own. Some of this learning came from mistakes. He says he's still learning, but it would have been great to have some of this wisdom back when he was a teenager.

His wife, Kathleen told him that her experience was similar. This kind of coaching can give a child huge advantages in life, but it's rare for a teenager to receive anything like it. It made Denny wish every young person could have a "wise uncle" or a "wise aunt." A kid could avoid a lot of trouble and misery by hearing these insights at the right time. And the long-term benefits would be enormous.

So he wrote a book called *Conversations with the Wise Uncle*. The book tells the fictional story of a teenager named Chris and his uncle Ray, who live in Little Rock, Arkansas. It includes conversations that took place during his middle school and high school years, the talks many kids never have.

Denny knew there needed to be a similar book for teen girls. But he had a boy's growing up experiences, and his own children included two sons and no daughters. So he asked his wife, Kathleen, to help him write this book. A writer herself, she grew up in a family of sisters, and she had mentored several young women.

If you're a teenager or approaching that time of life, maybe someone who cares about you gave you this book.

By now you probably no longer take everything adults say as gospel. That's probably a good instinct, because nobody has all the answers. And not too long from now you'll be an adult, so you need to get used to thinking for yourself.

But it would be a mistake to dismiss everything adults tell you. It makes more sense to listen, evaluate and then judge how useful the input is.

Not many young girls are lucky enough to have a wise, caring adult who will tell them the truth about the important things. That's why we wrote this book. It's the fictional story of Trisha and her aunt Maria, who live in Austin, Texas, and many of the conversations they had while Trisha was a teenager.

And it isn't a long book. It doesn't include every conversation Trisha and her aunt Maria would have had over the years.

Everybody's teen journey is different, so your own situation won't be exactly like Trisha's. Her life isn't your life. Her dreams aren't the same as your dreams. The story may be about someone else, but the insights are about you.

So take them seriously. Look over Trisha's shoulder while she learns things many kids your age haven't been told. Grab Aunt Maria's insights and make the most of them. They'll help you avoid many of the perils of growing up, guide you to become strong as a woman and give you a huge edge on life.

The Toothpicks of Time

Trisha stood outside the tall glass doors of the bank. To her right she saw a man in burnt-orange sweats getting money from an ATM machine. Through the glass she saw the bright lobby where her aunt Maria worked. She pushed the doors open and went in.

On the right was a long row of cashiers. On the left were several desks separated by low partitions. Her aunt sat at a desk in the far corner of the lobby, talking with a customer.

After a few minutes, they stood and shook hands, and the woman headed for the exit. Aunt Maria wore a dark grey business suit with a burgundy scarf. Her dark brown hair curved forward and touched her shoulders. When she saw Trisha standing in the lobby, she smiled and waved her over. Trisha hugged her aunt and sat in one of the chairs in front of the desk.

"I hope I'm not interrupting, Aunt Maria."

"No, Honey. Thanks for coming by. I wanted to talk to you. You look great! Were you playing tennis this morning?"

"Yes, my friend Aretha and I were on the courts by the river."

"How did it go?"

"I like playing with Aretha. She's a year older than I am, and she's been showing me some things."

"It would be fun for you and me to play together sometime."

"I don't know if I'm ready to play with you. You're so good."

"The truth is, I've been away from the court way too long. I could use the exercise. You'd be doing me a favor."

"That would be cool."

Maria looked at her niece. Trisha was taller than most girls her age. Her long, brown hair was gathered into a pony tail, and she had her mother's brown eyes. She sat up straight in the chair with her hands in her lap.

"You start the seventh grade this fall, right?"

"Right."

"Does your school have a tennis team?"

"No, but the high school does."

"Do you want to play on the team when you get to high school?"

"I don't think I'm good enough, Aunt Maria."

"Well, you have a couple more years to work on your game. You'd be surprised what you can learn between now and then. Your mom and I made the team as freshmen, and so can you."

"I hope so."

Aunt Maria smiled. "I'm sure of it. But listen, I want to talk to you about something else. One of my customers is a buyer, and he travels a lot. He was telling me about what a hassle it is to leave Johnson, his dog, at the kennel. It's expensive, and Johnson isn't happy there. I told him about you, that you've had pets all your life, and you might be willing to take care of

Johnson while he's gone. All you'd have to do is go over there twice a day to feed him and walk him and give him a little love. They live about three blocks from you, and he'd pay you $20 a day. What do you think?"

"Wow. What kind of dog is it?"

"Some kind of shepherd dog. He's cute, medium-sized. My friend says he's sweet."

"Do you think it would be okay with Mom?"

"I mentioned it to her, and she thinks it's a great opportunity."

"Can I see the dog first?"

"Of course! Do you want me to arrange it?"

"That would be great. Thanks, Aunt Maria."

"No problem. By the way, do you have an account here?"

"I've never had a bank account. I don't have much money."

"Well, if this job works out, you may have more, and you'll want a safe place to keep it. That's what a bank does. Plus, you get interest."

"Interest?"

"When you put money in a savings account, the bank regularly adds a little more to it. The more you put into your account, the more interest you make. For example, if you have a thousand dollars in your account, after a year they'll add ten or fifteen bucks to it, depending on the interest rate. It can add up. I can set up an account for you, if you want. Your mom and dad will help you open it."

"Mom said something about it once. Does it cost anything?"

"No. But you'll need to make your first deposit to open the account. Just come in with your mom or dad and bring some of your savings with you."

"Excellent. I'm going to have my own bank account!"

"Now. Have you had lunch?"

"No."

"Well, I'm hungry. Let's go to the barbecue place down the street."

"All right!"

After the waitress brought their food, Trisha was focused on taking big bites out of her barbecue sandwich.

"What do you think?" asked Maria.

"Pretty awesome. Terrific sauce."

"This little place has some of the best brisket in town, and it's not very well known. By the way, what's going on at home?"

"Elvis was throwing up a lot yesterday, and Mom took him to the vet. It was just hairballs, and the vet gave us something for him."

"Glad to hear it. By the way, do you know why your parents named him Elvis?"

"Because of Elvis Presley?"

Maria nodded. "Elvis was the original rock star. He was huge quite a few years before your mom and I were teenagers, but your mom was crazy about him anyway. Later, when you were little, she'd play her old Elvis tapes, and the two of you would sing. It was hilarious. So when she brought this little black kitty home, you sang your favorite Elvis song to him. 'I just wanna be...your teddy bear.' So your mom named him Elvis."

Trisha laughed. "I've heard that story before."

Aunt Maria stood up. "All this talk about the old days reminds me of something I've been wanting to talk to you about. Will you watch my purse? I'll be right back."

When she returned, she had a handful of toothpicks.

"What are those for, Aunt Maria?"

"I want to show you something."

She began placing the toothpicks end to end until there was a trail ten toothpicks long. She reached into her purse and removed a felt-tip pen. "Think of these ten toothpicks as a person's maximum lifespan. Do you know how old your grandparents are, Trisha?"

She thought about her grandparents, who lived in Dallas. She wasn't sure how old they were.

"Right now, I'm 42 years old," said Maria, making a mark at the beginning of the fifth toothpick. "My mom and dad are in their late sixties." She made a mark near the center of the seventh toothpick. "In our country, the average person lives about 85 years, plus or minus," she said and made another mark near the end of the ninth toothpick.

Then she said, "But your grandparents might live longer. Lots of people live into their nineties. Some live to be 100. Maybe you'll live to be 100, Trisha."

Trisha saw that Grandma and Grandpa still had a good stretch of time left.

"And this is you, right here." Aunt Maria made a mark near the left end of the second toothpick. She made a sweeping motion across the table, smiled and said, "You've got a lot of years in front of you!"

She continued. "You know Elvis Presley was a good-looking man. From the moment he first performed as a teenager the girls went absolutely nuts, screaming and crying while they watched him sing and shake on-stage. They called him 'The King of Rock and Roll' because back in the 50s his energy made rock music popular. What he was doing was really different. All rock music came after him. Of course he loved all the attention, all the money, and most of all the music. He loved performing."

"Wow."

"Do you know how old Elvis Presley was when he died?"

"No."

She pointed again to the forty-year mark. "He was the same age I am right now."

"You're kidding! Why did he die so young?"

"Well, he was like a lot of rock stars. He travelled a lot and did gigs practically every night and stayed up late with his buddies until dawn. They were so hyper they thought they needed pills to get to sleep. Then later they'd wake up hung over and take uppers to get pumped for the next performance. Elvis never thought about the consequences. One day he took too many drugs and that was that. The overdose killed him."

"That's terrible."

"Yes, it is. You know, many of his fans couldn't accept the fact that it happened. They rationalized that he got tired of show business and faked his death. There are still some people who believe he's alive somewhere."

"No kidding."

"So you see, Trisha, what I wanted to show you with these toothpicks is three things. First, that people don't live forever. Your life had a beginning, it will have a middle, and it will have an end. And no one knows for sure when or how their end will come, and neither will you. You aren't going to live forever, Trisha, so you have to make the best of the time you have. As a woman in her forties, I can tell you the time goes by way too fast. You have to treasure every day, every moment."

Trisha looked at the toothpicks and let that sink in. Then she looked up at her aunt and said, "What's the second thing?"

"The second thing is that you're at the very beginning of this journey." She pointed to the second toothpick. "Here you are right now. And here's where you'll be when you finish high school, and the plan is for you to go to college. That takes four years, which will put you right about here, age 22. By then hopefully you'll know what you want to do in life. Maybe you'll go to graduate school. Be a lawyer or an engineer. Who knows? That would take another two or three years. After that, you'll start your career, earning good money. See? You're not even thirty years old yet."

She moved her hand past the third toothpick. "After a while, you might meet a great guy and want to get married. And like your parents, you might have kids of your own. It's hard to say what you'll end up doing in life or what kind of career you'll have. But you still have a lot of time to figure it out, as you can see. Eventually, you'll retire, just as I hope to do down the road. By then, you'll be older than I am now. And later your own kids will get older and maybe they'll have kids, which would make you a grandmother. You could have a great life. A long life."

"And the third thing?"

Aunt Maria picked up the second toothpick and handed it to Trisha. "The third thing is that you're almost a teenager now, and I want to talk with you about something really important."

"About sex?"

"No, not sex, although that's important, and we can talk about it anytime you want. It's something else."

Trisha's heart started to beat faster. She wondered what her aunt had in mind.

"You're at the beginning of your teen years. Even though you have your whole life ahead of you, this time here while you're a teenager is probably the most important time you'll ever have."

"Really? All the good stuff happens later."

Aunt Maria laughed. "That's right. A lot of good stuff does happen later. But a lot of really important stuff is about to happen to you that can prepare you for all that good stuff, and I want you to know what it is."

"Like what?"

"Well for starters, you've been a girl for twelve years, going on thirteen. Now your body is about to grow into a woman's body. Your brain has a kind of biological clock in it, and the alarm is about to go off. That will trigger some chemicals called hormones to travel throughout your body. Growth hormones. It won't happen overnight, but your face is about to change into a woman's face, and your body is going to change into a woman's body."

"I'd like that."

"Yes. Eventually, you'll feel like a woman, too. You won't feel like a girl anymore."

Trisha tried to imagine a fully-grown version of herself. "That's fine with me."

"Growing up to be a woman takes time. And to be a successful woman takes effort, like becoming a good athlete. This time of growing up is a good thing, Trisha, a great thing. But it's not an easy thing. I'll tell you more about this sometime, some stuff I learned the hard way."

"Okay."

"But in addition to the hormones, there's one more thing that's about to change. It's not a change in your body. It's a change in your brain."

Trisha had no idea what Aunt Maria was talking about.

"Sweetheart, what I'm about to tell you is the most important thing you'll ever hear. Are you paying attention?"

"Yes."

For a moment, her aunt didn't say anything. She just looked at Trisha.

"Life is a joy, but it can also be dangerous and unforgiving. As you gradually become a woman, your parents will start letting you make your own decisions."

Trisha nodded.

"And as your body changes, your brain will change, too. The part of your brain that analyzes and makes decisions is about to enter a major growth phase. And if you do the work to learn to think well and decide well, it'll make it easier for you to make the right choices."

"What kind of work?"

"Have you ever seen a drawing or a picture of a brain?"

"Yeah."

"Well then, you know your brain is really complicated. It's a lot like a computer, but way more powerful than any computer on Earth. Every part of your brain works as a system to help you think. Everything you do, everything you say, everything you think and everything you feel is triggered by your brain. It's what makes you smart."

"Right."

"When you were born, you already had a complete brain. But the billions of tiny brain cells weren't connected up yet. It was like having a brand new computer with no software. As a baby, you learned to crawl by trying hard to crawl. You learned to walk by trying hard to walk. The same with learning how to talk, and so on. You learned all this by doing it. And all this effort caused your brain cells to physically wire together. You were programming your brain. Are you with me?"

"I think so."

"Good. Because there's one part of your brain that doesn't start final wiring until you're a teenager."

"What part is that?"

She placed the palm of her hand on her forehead. "It's this part right here. The last part of your brain to get wired is the part that makes you an exceptional learner, a logical thinker and a good decision-maker. Starting now and for about a dozen years, the connections you use here will become hard-wired. The ones you don't use will slowly wither away. All the other areas of your brain were constructed the same way. The brain cells that fire together will wire together, so it's use it or lose it. By the time you're in your early 20s, your basic foundation for critical thinking and decision-making will be set—for the rest of your life. If you spend the next ten years asking why and learning what causes what, your critical thinking ability will be huge. If all you do is have fun, fool around and do dumb things, it will be small. It's totally up to you."

"Will I stop learning after I grow up?"

"No. You can keep on learning until the day you die. The question is, how easy will it be for you to learn, to think well and make good decisions? Think of your ability to learn and the knowledge you'll gain as a house. If during adolescence you lay down a large foundation, you can build a large house on it. If you make a small foundation, then later as an adult you can only build a small house on it. Right now is the time when you start building this foundation. After you're a fully grown woman, you'll have to live with whatever foundation you constructed during high school and college."

Maria still had her hand on her forehead. "Now you put your hand on your forehead, too."

Trisha did so, but she took a quick look around. She felt a little silly doing it in the restaurant.

"There you go. Right behind your forehead is the front part of your brain—the part that helps you figure things out and make smart decisions."

"So what do I have to do to get more brain cells connected?"

"All you have to do is exercise that part of the brain as often as you can. Be a questioner. Try to understand what's going on in the world and why. Be someone who asks 'why' and 'what if' questions about everything. Why did this happen? How does this work? What if I try something different? Doing this will train your brain to think. So if you want to grow up smart, you've got to be Miss Curiosity."

"I don't think I'll have a problem with that. I'm already curious. I'm always asking questions about everything."

"I know you are. Keep doing that, Trisha. What happens to you along the rest of this path of toothpicks depends on it. The more you ask, the more you learn. The more you learn, the more you understand. You want to build the biggest possible platform for understanding. And there's one more way you can do that. It's actually the most important way."

"What's that?"

"Think about consequences. Get in the habit of asking yourself, 'If I do this, what will happen?' Say that back to me, Trisha."

"If I do this, what will happen?"

"Right. Always ask yourself that, and then imagine the consequences. Be conscious that you're about to make a choice, and that you're in charge of the choices you make. Will you promise me you'll always try to do that?"

"Sure, Aunt Maria. I promise."

"And if you feel the consequences are going to be bad, then don't go there."

"So before I do something, I think ahead. Think about what might happen if I do it."

"Exactly. And every time you do that, you'll be programming the front part of your brain."

For a few moments, Trisha and her aunt looked at each other without speaking. Then Maria said, "And there's another reason for doing that."

"It'll help me stay out of trouble."

"That's exactly right, Trisha. You'll be amazed at some of the dumb and dangerous things your friends are going to want to do in the years ahead. You'll be tempted to go along, because maybe they'll feel you don't belong if you don't. But some of them are going to get hurt, and some of them are going to get in trouble, and you don't want to be a part of it."

"Maybe it's not a good idea to have friends like that."

"That's a good point. And Trisha, there's another reason why doing the right thing isn't always going to be so easy. With the front part of your brain under construction, sometimes it won't be so easy to think things through logically and make the right decision. You'll have good intentions, but you'll feel like acting impulsively and reacting emotionally instead. Which is what teenagers often do."

"So what am I supposed to do?"

"Good question. You'll have two things going for you. First, you already know you need to ask 'why' and 'what if' questions. You know you need to think about consequences. Knowing what you need to do will actually help you do it. And I'll help you. I'll be your coach."

"Excellent."

"Other adults can help, too. A good teacher can help you ponder and analyze while you're learning. If you make the tennis team, your coach can help you think about tennis strategy. Your dad can help you solve problems, if you let him. And your mom. You're lucky to have such great parents, Trisha. The key is to take what they say seriously. Don't blow them off just because they're not telling you what you want to hear."

"I want to be smart like you, Aunt Maria."

Maria laughed. "You'll end up smarter than I am. I guarantee it."

Trisha wondered if her aunt was right. The idea that she could end up being that smart made her feel great.

"I'm glad we got to visit, Trisha. We talked about a lot of things in a short time. Plus a chance for you to earn more money and start saving and earning interest."

"Yes!"

"And this other opportunity that comes during the teen years, to build a foundation for critical thinking, to think through problems and make good decisions. To expand that part of your brain. Forever."

"Right."

"Or not."

"Right."

"So let's get going. You and I have places to go and people to see."

"The last part of your brain to get wired is the part that makes you an exceptional learner, a logical thinker and a good decision-maker. Starting now and for about a dozen years, the connections you use here will become hard-wired. The ones you don't use will slowly wither away. All the other areas of your brain were constructed the same way. The brain cells that fire together will wire together, so it's use it or lose it. By the time you're in your early 20s, your basic foundation for critical thinking and decision-making will be set—for the rest of your life. If you spend the next ten years asking why and learning what causes what, your critical thinking ability will be huge. If all you do is have fun, fool around and do dumb things, it will be small. It's totally up to you."

The Onion and the Full Plate

The Onion and the Full Plate

It was fall in Austin, and the unrelenting heat of the summer had been replaced by pleasantly cool days. So it didn't surprise Trisha when one Saturday morning she answered the doorbell and saw her aunt standing there in her tennis outfit.

"Hey, girl. Is your mom ready?"

"Ready for what?"

"Tennis. Robin said she wanted to play this morning."

"Mom, Dad and T.J. are out running errands. I thought they'd be back by now, but they're not."

Aunt Maria came in and closed the door behind her. "Oh, okay. How come you didn't go with them?"

"They're checking out end-of-year sales on gas grills. I'm so totally not interested."

"I understand. So what are you doing?"

"Nothing. I was taking a nap."

"Big night last night?"

"No, I was just bored, and I didn't feel like doing anything."

"That doesn't sound like you, Trisha. Is everything okay?"

Trisha looked down at her feet. "I brought my report card home yesterday. My grades were down, and Mom and Dad were on my case."

"How bad was it?"

"I got two A's, one in music and one in P.E. The rest were B's and C's. Maybe that's not such a bad report card, but I usually get all A's. They gave me a hard time about it, and I felt miserable."

"I'm sure you did. They must have been disappointed to see that you weren't doing your best."

"I guess so."

"Let's talk about it in the kitchen. If I'm not going to the courts right away, let's eat something. Are you hungry, too?"

"Not really."

They walked into the kitchen and Aunt Maria opened the refrigerator door.

"I see some left-over chicken. We could do something with that. Your folks will be back soon, and everyone could sit down and have lunch."

"Whatever."

"We can make chicken salad. Do you know how?"

"No."

"Do you like to cook?"

"I can cook some things."

"What's your specialty?"

"Omelets, I guess. I can make any kind of omelet."

"I love omelets. Well, I'll show you how I make chicken salad, and you can add that to your recipes."

"Okay."

"That's the spirit." Maria reached into the refrigerator and pulled out the plate of chicken. "Okay, we're also going to need an onion, a couple cloves of garlic, some mayo, and some dried cranberries. You got all that stuff?"

"I'll check."

"We'll make the sauce first. Then we'll chop up the other stuff and mix it up. The secret to great chicken salad is a great sauce. We'll need mayo and a little mustard and vinegar and plain yogurt. And some spices. Your mom usually has this stuff."

Aunt Maria guided Trisha through the preparation of the sauce. "I have a favorite place to get a chicken salad sandwich, and I decided to try making my own just like theirs. It was trial and error until I got the proportions right. Now taste this and tell me what you think."

Trisha put a little into a spoon. "Gosh, that's pretty good."

Maria scraped the chopped onion, garlic, cranberries and chicken into the sauce. "All right! Now mix that together."

She wiped the counters while Trisha stirred the salad.

"This looks yummy," said Trisha.

"Let's put it in the fridge to chill until your family gets here."

"Okay."

"Cooking is fun. And a girl's got to eat! I think of cooking as one of the life skills."

"A life skill?"

"That's what I call all the stuff you can learn that will help you make your way through life. You can survive without them, but life's a lot easier when you have the right skills. Like what we're doing right now—turning left-overs into a new meal."

"But there's more to life than cooking, Aunt Maria."

"That is so true, Trisha. A lot more. Like driving a car and using a computer. And how to work out in a gym and lift weights without hurting yourself. First aid."

"We have a first aid kit in the house and one in the car. Dad showed me how to use it."

"Also, manners and etiquette are life skills. They help you get along with people. In life, there's not much you can do if you don't know how to connect with people. And how to use tools and machines."

"I know how to mow the lawn. That's one of my chores."

"Fantastic. A lot of people think outside work is guy stuff, but that's nonsense. A woman needs to know how to take care of herself. Who knows when you'll get married or what he'll be good at. There are dozens and dozens of life skills. It's the idea that knowledge is power. You know how to do stuff or you don't. I think it's smart to start when you're young."

"Maybe they should teach life skills in school instead of some of this boring stuff I have to learn. It's hard to make an A when it's boring."

"Which ones are boring?"

"Like math."

"Yes, math can be boring, especially if your teacher isn't giving you real projects to learn from. Then it can be fun. Even exciting."

"Well, Mr. Macy is boring."

"I'm sorry to hear it. But you know what?"

"What?"

"You shouldn't blame Mr. Macy."

"Why not? He's the teacher. It's his job to make us learn."

"Do you really think somebody can make you learn? If you decided you didn't care about a subject and you weren't going to make the effort, what could a teacher do to force you to learn it anyway?"

Trisha thought about that for a moment. "I don't know."

"The truth is, no one can make you learn. And no one can keep you from learning. If you're really interested or if you make up your mind to master something, nobody can stop you. When it comes to learning, you're in charge, not the teacher."

"I never thought of it that way."

"Trisha, you're going to have some wonderful teachers, and you're going to have some who are, well, boring. And everything in between. The students who come out on top are those who just accept it and learn anyway."

"But why should I learn stuff I don't care about? Stuff I'm never going to use?"

"Do you remember when we talked about developing the smart part of your brain by asking why and what if questions?"

"Sure."

"So here's a why question for you. Why should you go ahead and learn math skills, and for that matter any other subject they might put in front of you?"

Trisha gave that some thought. Then she said, "I guess maybe I'll probably end up needing to know some of this stuff, even if I can't imagine it right now."

"That's good. Can you think of an example?"

Trisha frowned. "Nothing comes to mind right now."

"Okay. How about this. Someday you might want to buy something expensive, like a car, and you'd want to know which of several cars is the best value. You'd need to calculate the cost of standard features versus add-on features, plus hidden costs like loan interest, insurance, fuel and maintenance in order to do a comparison. You'd need math skills for that."

"Maybe so."

"Can you think of any other reasons for learning things you think are boring?"

"Maybe these are just things I ought to know, whether they're fun or not."

"Good point. You need to know about the world you live in, Trisha. Once you're an adult and on your own, you either get what's going on or you're clueless. It's not really about becoming a mathematician or an expert in history. It's about understanding how the world works."

"Okay."

"But I can think of another, more important reason to learn something like math. It's because math is a logical thought process, so it forces you to think logically. It's as if the math isn't actually as important as what learning it does to your brain. It makes you a better thinker."

"Hmm."

"So, Trisha, don't let your teacher hold you back. Take whatever you can from Mr. Macy and do the rest yourself. You can take responsibility for your own learning. Learn it anyway. Get your A anyway."

"Gosh, Aunt Maria, that was some pep talk!"

"I told you I was going to be your coach."

Trisha laughed.

"I'm glad to see you're not so down in the dumps anymore. So while you're in a good mood, I want to tell you a few more things about what you need to learn while you're still a teenager. Would you hand me the other half of that onion, please?"

Trisha gave it to her and her aunt set it on a plate.

"Talking about your education and life skills made me think of this onion."

Trisha smiled and looked up at her aunt.

"You see, this onion here is like you and me. It's got layers. We've got layers, too. We go through life, and we learn stuff. Every time we learn something important, it's like adding to the layers. What we learn becomes a part of us. Like learning how to cook or how to use tools. What we learn adds thickness to the layers."

"So the layers in the onion represent what we learn."

"Exactly. And if you're lucky, you'll never stop learning."

Her aunt put the onion in front of her. "You can see this onion has six layers, including the core. Think of the first three layers as kinds of learning that you and everybody else are pretty familiar with. I'll mention those first."

She picked up the knife and pointed at the outer layer. "You see this ring? Think of this one as knowledge and skills you need for your career. For example, if you end up being a lawyer, then this is what you need to know to practice law. If you're a doctor, like a surgeon or a dentist, then this layer is medical know-how. If you become a pilot, then the outer layer represents how to fly an airplane. It's about getting good at your business. You might learn some of this in college, but most of it you learn later, on the job."

"So if I want to be a musician, I'd have to learn the music business."

"You got it. But there's a whole lot more you need to know to be successful."

"Like what?"

She pointed the knife at the second layer. "Let's call this next layer your formal education, the stuff you're learning now, and later in high school and college. Some of your education may help in your career, but most of it is pretty general. All those courses in history, literature, writing, math, art, and science teach you how the world works. Basic stuff. Business know-how comes later, when you get into your career."

Trisha pointed at the onion. "So I learn this now. And this outer ring is what I learn later, while I'm working."

"Right."

"What are the other rings for?"

Aunt Maria moved the knife to the next ring. "This ring represents life skills, what we were talking about before. Using tools, operating machines, organizing a work space, safe driving, managing your money. How to dress and take care of your clothes. There are a gazillion life skills."

"Aunt Maria?"

"Yes?"

"If they don't focus on life skills in school, and if there are a ton of them, how am I supposed to learn all that?"

"That's such a good question. The answer is, it takes a long time to learn the life skills you're going to need. You just accept that you need to work on it and you go after one skill at a time. Some people grow up with very few life skills. In a way, they're handicapped. So if you start learning these skills as a teenager, it puts you way ahead of the game."

"Okay."

Aunt Maria tapped the face of the onion with the knife. "So it's typical for people to acquire business know-how, basic education and life skills—the outer three rings. Your world is set up fairly well to help you in these areas, if you take advantage of it. But the next three layers— the inner ones—are not consciously taught in most families, schools or businesses. You and I are going to concentrate on them on our own, because they're even more important than the other three. For example, this next layer here is about critical thinking skills."

"What's that?"

"Remember when we talked about problem-solving and decision-making, the front part of your brain that's under construction?"

"Yeah."

"That's what I'm talking about—your ability to do higher level thinking. Not understanding how things work, but why. Figuring out what causes what. Analyzing a situation and choosing the best way to act. Solving a problem. Imagining future consequences. Coming up with a plan of action."

"Right. You said you were going to help me."

"What I'm planning to do is coach you—to think for yourself as we do things together. You learn to think by thinking, just as you get better at tennis by playing tennis."

"I get it."

"There are two more layers that are not consciously addressed with young people. This next ring has to do with knowing how to relate to people. It's called people skills. It's the skills involved in communicating with others. How to listen, how to keep an open mind when someone is talking to you, how to resolve a conflict, how to praise and encourage people, how to tell someone when you don't like what they're doing. Because if you don't deal with these situations right, things don't go well. The truth is, a lot of people have trouble with people skills, because they aren't taught in schools."

"Why not?"

"Beats me. I think they should be. They're important in every aspect of life where people are involved—school, friendships, work, family, marriage—virtually everything. Adults who have good people skills rise quickly in their careers. It's a game-changer, Trisha."

"Are you going to teach me some people skills?"

"I can coach you. Actually, I'm still catching up in this department myself, after all these years."

"Well it looks like we've run out of rings. All that's left is the core. I think of this area here, right smack in the middle of the onion, as being strong as a person."

"You mean working out?"

"Actually, it is a lot like working out. Only instead of physical strength, you work on inner strength. Having strong character."

Trisha thought about that. She liked the idea of being strong. But she wasn't sure what her aunt meant by "being strong as a person."

"You know how doing the right thing almost always means doing the hard thing? Like telling the truth when the truth is embarrassing? Or being patient when you're in a hurry? Or staying focused on a task or getting your homework done when you'd rather be having fun? This is what is called personal strength, being strong as a person."

"Do you think I'm strong as person?"

"I think you are, Sweetheart, in many ways. For example, instead of goofing off, you're usually working on getting better at something. Like your tennis. That takes focus. And effort. And commitment and patience. It would be a whole lot easier to just fool around and have fun."

"But I like to have fun."

"And you should. Life should be fun. But life is challenging, too, and it takes personal strength to get through the tough times and achieve your goals. Most things worth having don't come easy."

"Friends are worth having, and making friends is easy."

"That's good. But having a best friend takes effort, and keeping friends over the years isn't so easy, as you'll find out. You're right. Some good things are easy. Like appreciating nature, for example. But for some reason, you have to work like crazy to get most things worth having. I'm not sure why that is, but it's true."

"I've been trying to save money for a guitar."

"I didn't know you were interested. That's terrific!"

"The really good ones are expensive, and I don't have enough."

"But you're still working at it. You haven't given up. It takes strength to persevere."

"And I want to learn how to play it."

"I know. And every time you learn something it makes you stronger. There's a lot to learn." Aunt Maria held up the onion. "All these layers of ability help you succeed in life, but I think these three inner layers—personal strengths, people skills and critical thinking skills—are most important to your success. Think about it, Trisha. If you aren't strong deep inside, if you don't have courage, if you can't keep your cool, if you can't accept the truth, if you don't stay optimistic—in other words, if you don't do the hard things in life, then the other layers of learning won't count for much. If you aren't good with people, it will be hard to work with others and have good relationships. If you can't think straight, you won't understand what's happening around you and your decisions will get you in trouble."

She nodded. "I guess I have a lot to learn."

"Everyone does. When I got my first job in a bank I was way behind the learning curve. In fact, I'm still learning, still adding to my layers of ability. But you've got time. The more you learn while you're a teenager, the easier it's going to be for you later. Start now, get a head start, and you'll have a huge advantage when you're grown up. A lot of kids waste their teen years."

Then Aunt Maria began taking the onion apart, starting with the outer layers. She put each layer on the plate, one at a time.

"You've got a full plate, Trisha. That's what we say when someone has a lot to do and it seems like more than the average person can do."

"It seems like a lot."

"It is. But there's one thing on this plate that's more important than anything else. It's so important that you should consciously work on it now, because you'll need to keep learning and growing until the day you die. You know what it is?"

"The smart part of my brain?"

"Well yes, critical thinking skills are terribly important, but I'd make that number two. To me, the most important area of development is the core of the onion. It's who you are as a person. Your character. Personal strengths. There are lots of ways to be strong as a person, and if you exercise them often enough, they become a habit, a part of who you are, and it'll be easier for you to do the right things, the hard things in life."

"I don't want to fall behind. I want to be really good at what I do."

"You can and you will. In my opinion, you're off to a great start. I've told you things most kids never hear. And I know other people who can help you. We're not going to wait until you're grown up."

"Thanks, Aunt Maria."

"You bet. We're going to keep you ahead of the learning curve, Trisha."

❖

A Teen's Full Plate of Learning

In addition to life skills
and formal education...

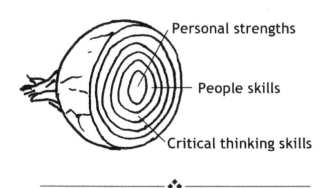

Personal strengths

People skills

Critical thinking skills

❖

———————————— ❖ ————————————

"The truth is, no one can make you learn. And no one can keep you from learning. If you're really interested or if you make up your mind to master something, nobody can stop you. When it comes to learning, you're in charge, not the teacher."

———————————— ❖ ————————————

Strong for Tennis

The following summer Trisha and her aunt were playing tennis.

"Fifteen-thirty," said Trisha, as she bounced the ball in front of her twice. Then she tossed it softly, cranked her racquet back and smacked the ball on the way down.

It curved sharply over the net, and Aunt Maria met it with a solid forehand that sailed past Trisha.

"Unh!" she grunted in frustration. "I should have gotten back to center more quickly. Fifteen-forty."

She repeated her serving ritual, once again sending the ball solidly over the net. This time her aunt scooted to the right to hit a backhand shot, but her stroke was too late and the ball rocketed off the court.

"Good serve!"

"Thanks," said Trisha. "Thirty-forty."

She served again, delivering the ball safely to the other side of the net. Aunt Maria returned it in front of Trisha, who hit it squarely with a forehand. But her aunt had moved to the net and she met the ball with a solid volley that sent it rebounding out of Trisha's reach.

"Great shot, Aunt Maria. That's game. And set! You win. But we're playing another set, right? I'll beat you next time."

"I think maybe you will, Kiddo. It's harder to beat you than it used to be."

"Mom's been coaching me."

"You have quite a serve there. The ball is almost always in play, which keeps me on my toes. Very consistent! But before we play another set, let's take a water break."

"I've got some water in my bag," said Trisha.

"Okay. Let's sit in the shade."

After they toweled off and had some water, Trisha said, "Aunt Maria?"

"Yes, Dear?"

"Were you going easy on me?"

"Oh my goodness no. I guess I used to when you were little, but I play to win now. And I'm getting a good workout."

"I don't want you to ever go easy on me."

"I wouldn't be doing you any favors if I did."

"Good. I want to get better, and I think I am. But I'm still not good enough to make the team. I know lots of girls who can beat me."

"Maybe you should play them sometime."

"I do, sometimes. But Aunt Maria, could you show me some ways to improve my game?"

"You mean technique?"

"Yeah."

"Well, I don't know. Your fundamentals look pretty good to me. I'm not a tennis coach, you know. Your mom seems to have done a pretty good job with you so far."

"Yeah, Mom's great. I'm learning good stuff. But I was hoping you noticed something I could do better."

Aunt Maria didn't answer right away. Then she said, "Can I see your racquet?"

"Sure," said Trisha, and handed it to her.

Her aunt hefted it. "It seems light to me, compared to mine."

"I've had it for three years," said Trisha. "I like it."

"It's a nice racquet. Probably perfect for you right now. But you've probably noticed how your body's growing. There will come a time when you'll want to get a mid-sized racquet with better balance."

"You think?"

"At the right time, a new racquet could kick your game up a notch."

"Wow, maybe I should start looking for one!"

"Maybe. But to get the power you want, you'll need more upper body strength. Your family goes to the YMCA, don't they?"

"Yes. Mom goes three or four times a week. But I haven't been going regularly."

"Well, I guess that's my tip for the day. Keep working on your tennis skills with your mom, but get your mom to show you how to develop your body for tennis."

"Some of the older girls I've played with have great bodies. I just thought I'd look like that after a while, just from playing."

"Strength is as important to tennis as technique and skill. You have to be strong enough to hit the kind of shots that will beat a worthy opponent. And to move more quickly around the court. Tennis is a physical game."

Trisha nodded. "How long do you think it'll take for me to get that strong?"

"If you're serious about tennis and you want to make the team, I'd get into a workout routine as soon as possible. This week. Get a good every-other-day routine going, and every couple weeks try to increase what you're doing. You'll begin adding strength as you do more work. You can borrow my racquet when you want to see if you're ready."

Trisha took a long drink of water and said, "Thanks, Aunt Maria. That's good advice."

"Well then, while we're on a roll, there's one more thing—something else that counts more than anything."

"What?"

"It's the game between the ears."

"The game between the ears?"

"Your mom and I learned about this when we were on the high school tennis team. It goes like this. When you're on the court across the net from a good player, ultimately it comes down to whether you're strong inside. Whether you've got the personal strengths to hang in there and play your best game when the match gets tough."

"What do you mean?"

"Say you hit a bad shot. Say you don't react fast enough and you hit it into the net and you're down love-forty. How do you react in that situation? Do you get upset with yourself? How long do you let it bother you? If you let your emotions boil over, it'll affect your next shot. I saw that a couple times today. One bad shot led to another."

"I'm just being tough on myself. I'm trying to get better."

"I know. But when a person's mind is filled with frustration, anger, worry and other negative emotions, it isn't clear and calm, which is what you need in order to focus on the next shot. This is the mental aspect of the game—the game between the ears. In tennis, your opponent is doing everything possible to keep you off your game, to get you to make mistakes, and how you react is what makes the difference. The best players sometimes do get angry, just like you. But they've learned how to channel their emotions—to clear their minds, walk away from the previous shot, and focus on the here and now."

"I've seen players do that. So how do you improve your mental game?"

"Before I tell you about the mental game, I'd like to say a little more about personal strengths. We talked about this in the kitchen, the core of the onion, remember?"

"Yes."

"First, there are dozens of personal strengths. Each one has to do with doing the right thing, which often means doing the hard thing. Every sport, in fact every aspect of life, no matter what, requires strong core strengths—certain key personal strengths. You could be a doctor, a lawyer, a teacher, a mechanic, or a parent. Different strengths for different activities. Some of these strengths are important for playing competitive tennis."

"Okay."

"Did you bring anything to write with?"

"In my purse."

"Okay. When I mention an area of personal strength, it will be easier to remember it if you make a note of it. The first is perseverance."

"Perseverance."

"When I was in high school, my tennis coach showed us a video of the 1980 Wimbledon final. It was an amazing battle between two great champions, Björn Borg and John McEnroe. McEnroe started strong, winning the first set. But then Borg won the next two sets and was about to win the third set and the match. He had McEnroe down 5-4, but McEnroe saved five match points to make it 5-5. Although Borg survived six set points, after a 22-minute tie-breaker McEnroe eventually won the set to even the match at two sets each. This was a huge setback for Borg. He was only one point from winning Wimbledon, and now the match was even. In the fifth set, McEnroe seemed to be cruising to victory, and he was about to break Borg's serve, 15-40. But then Borg refused to give up. He dug deep and reeled off 19 straight points on serve to win the set and the match, his fifth consecutive Wimbledon victory.

"The memory of that has always inspired me to be tough and to never give up. My opponent might be one point away from beating me. The danger is that I might think, 'Oh well, I can't win now.' But if I let myself believe that, I won't make the effort. I won't be able to win. Perseverance is when you get the urge to give up, and you don't. You keep trying. You keep giving it your absolute best."

"I wish I'd seen that match."

"It was one of the greatest tennis matches of all time. Check the internet. I'll bet some of the good parts are posted. Maybe the whole thing."

"Good idea."

"To win in tennis you also need composure. It's all about channeling negative emotions aside. Not letting your emotions affect what you do next. You'll feel the emotions. Everybody does. But if you can't let go of them right away, if you can't calm down and concentrate on your shot, you're toast."

"Stay calm, cool and collected," said Trisha.

"Right. Another personal strength tennis players need is self-confidence. Often in a match the shot you need will be a tough one. Maybe it's a delicate drop shot when your opponent is behind the baseline. Maybe it's a hard forehand to the corner. Confidence means believing you can make that shot. If you doubt whether you can, you probably won't do what you have to do to make it. You can't talk yourself into being confident. You have to earn it. It comes from having made similar shots before, whether in practice or competition. And then giving yourself credit for that. It's easy to think that something hard can't be done. You have to know you can do it."

"Is it over-confidence when you believe you can do it even if you don't know what you're doing?"

"Yes, it is. But I think over-confidence is better than not believing in yourself at all. With over-confidence you at least give yourself a chance. You might accidentally make the shot, or your opponent might make a mistake. At least the over-confident person is trying. Believe it or not, a lot of people have good skills, but in a match they still doubt their ability to win. They don't give themselves credit."

"So the key is to give yourself credit for what you can do."

"Exactly. Another strength is awareness. You keep your head in the game and pay attention to what your opponent is doing and getting ready to do. And a related one is focus. When the ball is coming at you, you focus on the ball and how you want to hit it. Nothing else. Not the weather, not your friends, not games on other courts, not shots you made earlier. You stay in the moment."

"That's a lot to think about."

"Yes, it is. You may need to think about your inner game at first. But the more you exercise these strengths, the easier they get. Eventually they become routine. You just act that way on the court without thinking about it. So, which one of these is your strong suit? Which strength do you engage most often, automatically?"

Trisha looked down at her notes. Perseverance, composure, self-confidence, awareness, and focus. She could see how all of them would help her win at tennis. She thought maybe she needed to get stronger in every area.

"Perseverance is my best, I guess. Mom kind of drilled that into me. 'Don't be a quitter,' she'd say."

"Your mom's right. If you give up trying to win a game, guess what will happen."

"I'll lose."

"That's right. But even more important, you'll get in the habit of quitting. You'll feel it's okay to give up in other situations. In school. In a job. In relationships. Personal strengths aren't just important in sports. They're behavior patterns that affect all aspects of your life. If you give up, you'll start thinking of yourself that way—as a quitter. You won't like who you are. And you won't accomplish things you're capable of."

"I don't think of myself as a quitter."

"I don't either, Trisha. Now which of the strengths do you feel you need to work on the most?"

She looked at the list again. "All of them."

"Pick the one you'd like to work on first. You can't work on all of them at the same time. You'll spread yourself too thin."

"Self-confidence, I guess. I never feel confident when I'm playing with somebody who's better than I am. I'm always worried my mistakes will kill me."

"Good choice. You know, a lot of people don't give themselves enough credit. They have their strong points, but they don't acknowledge them. So they doubt their ability to do things. If you want to be more confident, you have to really believe you're good at certain things. You need to get in the habit of saying to yourself, 'I can do this.'"

"Get cocky."

"Yeah, just do it. You see, a personal strength is a lot like a skill, like hitting a shot with top spin. You want to get to the point that you do the right thing automatically. The only way to get to that point is to do it a lot."

"Exercise the strength."

"Exactly! And there's one more step."

"What's that?"

"Later, whether the match went well or not, think about what you did. Ask yourself what happened, why, what were the consequences, and how you can improve on that. This is how you coach yourself to learn from experience."

"So I do it for real, then I think about it."

"That's right—cycles of action and reflection. It's like working out in a gym. You gotta do the reps. If you do, you'll get stronger. Only instead of working on physical strength, you're working on personal strength."

"I get it."

"So. Are you ready for another set? Another chance to beat me?"

"Yeah!"

Walking back to the court, Aunt Maria put her arm around Trisha's shoulders. "Before we get started, I want to level with you about something."

"What?"

"You already have the ability to beat me— right now. You've never done it before, but right now, in this set, you can beat me. Do you understand what I'm saying? Do you believe me?"

Trisha squinted at her aunt, but she didn't say anything.

"You can beat me. When you accept that truth, that's when you'll actually do it."

---❖---

"I'm talking about the mental aspect of the game—the game between the ears. In tennis, your opponent is doing everything possible to keep you off your game, to get you to make mistakes, and how you react is what makes the difference. The best players sometimes do get angry, just like you do. But they've learned how to channel their emotions—to clear their minds, walk away from the previous shot, and focus on the here and now."

---❖---

❖

– REFLECTION –
Take ACTION, then ask yourself
"The Five Magic Questions"

What happened?
Why did it happen that way?
What were the consequences?
What should I do differently in the
future?
What are my next steps?

❖

"You gotta do the reps."

ACTION – REFLECTION
ACTION – REFLECTION
ACTION – REFLECTION
ACTION – REFLECTION
ACTION – REFLECTION
ACTION – REFLECTION
ACTION – REFLECTION

❖

A Nice Way to Say No

Aunt Maria drove up Rockpile Lane and stopped at a one-story gray brick home with green shutters. A steady rain was falling, and Trisha had called her at the bank asking if it was convenient to pick her up after work. Maria honked twice.

A couple minutes later Trisha appeared in the doorway and waved. She hugged her friend and then ran to the car, holding a guitar case to her chest.

"Hi, Aunt Maria! Thanks for picking me up."

Maria backed the car out of the driveway. "It's no trouble. Is that your dad's guitar? How are you doing with it?"

"Dad's been showing me some things. I love it. He says I have good hands for the guitar."

"Maybe you can play me something when I come over Saturday night."

"Maybe. I'm just a beginner, you know." "That's okay. I think it would be fun. By the way, I know what I want to get you for your birthday. You'll be thirteen, and I want my gift to be special."

"Whatever it is, I'll love it."

"Well, here's what I have in mind. You've been working out, and you're a lot stronger than you were the last time we played tennis together."

"I am. A trainer at the gym showed me what I need to do, and I'm getting in shape for tennis."

"I'd like to take you downtown to pick out your dream racquet, and I want to get you two. You need two for competition."

"Oh wow," said Trisha. She gazed through the windshield. Finally, she said, "Aunt Maria?"

"Yes?"

"I'm thrilled you want to do this." She hesitated, then started again. "I'm thrilled, but Mom already said she was going to get me a new racquet and some other tennis stuff."

"Why, that's lovely, Trisha. Your mom and I must be on the same page. Can I get you something else? Do you have anything in mind?"

"Actually, there's something I want more than a tennis racquet."

"Tell me."

"I want my own guitar. A really good one. I like playing the guitar a lot more than I thought I would, and I've started saving all my pet-sitting money to buy one. But I don't want you to buy it for me, because the one I want is too expensive. It costs about three thousand dollars, and right now I only have about three hundred. If you could help me save for it, that would be the best gift ever."

"Goodness, Trisha, I didn't realize you cared so much about it."

"I do. I want to learn to play more than anything."

"That's great, Trisha. To be passionate about something like the guitar is a wonderful thing. Of course I'll help you. I was planning on spending about four hundred dollars for the racquets, so if you like, I'll just put that money into your savings account."

Trisha squealed and bounced in her seat. "Oh thank you, Aunt Maria! What a wonderful gift!"

"I'm tickled to help out. You'll have to show me this guitar sometime, the one you want. So does this mean you have two passions now? Tennis and the guitar?"

"I really like them both, for different reasons." said Trisha.

"Then you're doubly blessed."

"I was learning some new things at Ginger's house this afternoon."

"Oh, so that's why you have the guitar with you. Does she play, too?"

"No, it's her older brother, Michael. He's really good, and he volunteered to show me some things."

"What have you learned?"

"He likes to play a few notes, then show me how he did it. Then I try it while he coaches me. Today he showed me how to pull off."

"Pull off?"

"It's just a technique to go from one note to another in a smooth way to get a good sound."

"Sounds like you're really into it, Trisha."

"Whenever he shows me stuff I go home and practice. He's very patient. And sweet."

"Sweet?"

"It's easy to talk to Michael. We talk about all kinds of stuff. He's a sophomore, but he treats me like an equal. He turns off his cell phone when he's showing me something, and when he corrects me he doesn't laugh at me or put me down. And he's cute."

Aunt Maria pulled the car into the driveway of Trisha's house. It was still raining hard.

"Trisha, I've been meaning to talk to you about something, and now seems like a good time. Do you have a few minutes before you go in?"

"Sure. What's up?"

"I want to talk to you about boys. Just a few things I think every young girl ought to know, and I want to be sure you do. Do you mind talking about this?"

"You want to give me the sex talk? Mom's already told me about sex, but I don't mind hearing what you have to say."

"No, I'm sure your mom did a good job explaining the basics. I'm more interested in talking about boys and how they think about sex."

"This ought to be interesting," Trisha said with a grin.

"It is."

"Okay, shoot."

"Well, when it comes to sex, most boys don't think of it the way girls do."

"What do you mean?"

"Well, for one thing, the idea that sex can lead to pregnancy doesn't bother a boy in the same way that it bothers a girl, because it's the girl who gets pregnant, not the boy. It's the girl who has to have the baby and take care of it."

"Don't they care?"

"Yes, but they don't fully appreciate what their role would be if it happened. The hard stuff isn't going to happen to them. So a girl has to look out for herself. Boys are thinking about something else."

"Like what?"

"He's got his mind on how much he wants to have sex. How good it will feel, what it will be like. That's about as far as it goes for a typical teenage boy. And it's not his fault. Do you know what causes feelings of sexual desire?"

"Love?"

"That's probably how most girls look at it. But the desire to have sex is a physical urge caused by the presence of the hormone testosterone. The more testosterone you have in your body, the stronger the urge to have sex. It's biology. This is true for both men and women. Testosterone production is one of the body changes you experience as a teenager. It's why you start thinking about sex at this age."

"So if both boys and girls are starting to think about sex, what's the difference?"

"The difference is that boys have about ten times as much testosterone as girls."

"Wow! They must have sex on their brains a lot."

"Honey, you have no idea. It's true that girls think about sex from time to time; but for most boys, thinking about sex is like background music playing in their minds."

"It's hard to imagine."

"Yes. You don't feel about sex the same way they do. Which is why I wanted to talk with you. To manage your relationships with boys, there are some things you need to do."

"I'm all ears."

"Okay. First of all, you need to be the one who sets boundaries in a relationship."

"Boundaries? What kind of boundaries?"

"I'll explain, but first do you mind if I ask you a couple questions about Michael?"

"Sure, go ahead."

"Do you like him in a romantic way? Is he a boyfriend?"

"No. He's nice. I haven't known him very long, and I don't think he's interested in me that way. It's just a lot of fun learning the guitar from him."

"Is that okay with you? You don't want him to be your boyfriend?"

"Not really. He's a little old for me."

"So you've set some boundaries with him."

"What do you mean?"

"I mean it sounds like you've decided you want to do certain things with Michael, such as learn to play the guitar. But you draw the line at other things, like kissing or dating."

Trisha went silent. She frowned as she looked at her fingernails.

"Did I say something that upset you?"

"No. It's just that I haven't thought about Michael like that."

"We don't need to talk about this now if you don't want. Does it make you feel uncomfortable?"

"No, it's all right."

"I only mentioned Michael because you said he was sweet. Usually when a girl says that, she really likes the boy. Has he ever kissed you?"

Trisha glanced over at her aunt, and then began examining her fingernails again.

"He did try to kiss me once, but I didn't know if I wanted him to, so I asked him to stop."

"And did he?"

"Yes. We talked about it. He said I was pretty and sometimes he just felt like kissing me. I told him it scared me a little and maybe we better not. So he never tried it again. But I think he probably wants to."

"How about you? Do you want to?"

"I've imagined kissing him. It might be exciting, but I keep thinking I'd better not."

"Why not?" said Aunt Maria.

"I don't know. Maybe I'm not ready."

"Well, Honey, I think that's an honest answer. And I think your instincts are natural and good. It's a good thing to like boys, and it's natural to want to kiss a boy you care about."

"But I don't think about Michael that way."

"I understand. I'm sure Michael is a fine young man, but from his point of view you're a really pretty girl, and physically you're more mature than most girls your age. So when he's with you, I guarantee that he has thoughts about sex. As I said, it's nothing against him. It's the way the male body works."

"I want it to be about the guitar, not sex."

"It can be, Trisha. Michael's not an animal. He has urges, but he's an intelligent human being. He has the ability to think and make choices. He can control his behavior."

"But will he?"

"That's where boundaries come in. You not only need to draw the line for yourself, you need to tell him where the line is. You tell him what you want and don't want. For example, with Michael you could say something like, 'I want you to know you're a terrific person, and I love coming over to learn from you. To me, you're like the older brother I wish I had. And that's how I'd like it to stay between us. Not boyfriend-girlfriend. No more kissing or anything. I like our friendship just the way it is, and I don't want to change it. I hope you feel the same way.' Something like that. You draw the line. You make sure he knows what's okay and what's not okay. Basically, it's saying no, but in the nicest possible way. Do you think you can do that?"

"I think so."

"This doesn't mean you should go through your whole life as a teenager without getting kissed. After all, you might care about a boy sometime."

"I hope so," said Trisha. "When the time comes I want to go on dates and maybe even have a boyfriend."

"That will happen someday. The thing is, when it does, you want to know how to handle yourself. Sexual feelings are strong, and if you're kissing and touching each other, the two of you could get carried away. It happens all the time."

"I'll have to draw the line."

"Exactly. But where?"

"It seems to me that kissing is no big deal."

"Personally, I think kissing is a big deal, in a nice way. But kissing can get pretty steamy. It can quickly lead to touching. And once you get excited, it's hard to say no. If you don't want him to do this, you have to draw the line at kissing."

"But it must be weird to talk with a guy about this."

"You wouldn't bring it up when you're first getting to know each other. But later, if you realize you have feelings for each other, he might want to touch you where you don't want to be touched. He might want to have sex. You need to be the one to tell him what's okay and what's not okay. Your boyfriend probably won't be the one to set limits. Most boys aren't made that way. They want to get past first base."

"What do you mean?"

"That's how some boys talk about it with each other. First base is kissing. Second base is sexual touching. They get to third base when they get her pants off. You can guess what home plate is all about."

"Gross."

"When a teenage boy pushes a girl to have sex, he may say things about love. But for most boys the real goal isn't a long-term relationship. What he wants, deep down, is to have sex. For him, it's like climbing a mountain. When he finally reaches the top, he's satisfied. He's done. In fact, it often happens that the boy loses interest in the girl after he has sex with her, because he got what he wanted. He starts looking for another mountain. This would make any girl feel awful, because she thought the relationship meant more than that.

"And just as bad, some boys like talking about their sexual adventures with their friends. Then the story gets passed along, and a lot people find out about it. This could damage the girl's reputation."

"Oh, Aunt Maria, is it really this way?"

"I'm afraid so. Later, when boys mature into men, the good ones have learned more about women and how to treat them right. Sex is a wonderful thing. But there are risks, and you need to take charge of your relationships."

"Aunt Maria, did you have sex when you were a teenager?"

"I was tempted a couple times, I have to admit. But no, I didn't. Mostly I was afraid I'd get pregnant. So I didn't have sex until I was an adult. And I'm glad you haven't. In spite of what some kids say, most girls don't have sex until after high school. And that's smart. Even if the boy uses a condom, you can still get pregnant. It happens. When teenagers have sex, they ignore their front brain altogether. They can forget about the consequences, which can be enormous. Getting pregnant before you get married is one of the most difficult things that can happen to you."

Trisha looked out the window a moment. "I guess I'd either have to get an abortion or have the baby, so either way it would be bad news. I can't even imagine walking around school all fat and pregnant. Ugh!"

"You're right. If you got pregnant and chose to have the baby, your life would change forever. You'd have to say goodbye to your normal life of school and having fun."

"Aunt Maria, get real! I'm just a kid! I don't know how to take care of a baby. That would be a total joke."

"You're right, Honey, you're way too young to be a mother. But pregnancy isn't the only risk. There's STDs."

"STDs?"

"Sexually transmitted diseases."

"Oh, mom mentioned venereal disease, but I don't know much about it."

"If the boy you had sex with already had sex with somebody else, that person could have infected him with a sexually transmitted disease, like HIV. HIV can kill you."

"I know."

"Or gonorrhea, or syphilis, or chlamydia, or herpes. He could infect you. You could get painful sores on your private parts."

"Ick!"

"Trisha, there's a bottom line to this."

"What?"

"The bottom line is that someday you'll want to have sex with a man because you care deeply about him and want to be intimate. But it's smart to wait until you're an adult and ready to have a fully committed relationship."

"That's how I feel about it."

"I'm glad. You're growing up, and it's important that you take care of yourself. Well, I gotta get going. Your uncle Larry's expecting me. Say hi to your mom. And the next time I see you I hope you'll play me something on that guitar."

---❖---

"You draw the line. You make sure he knows what's okay and what's not okay. Basically, it's saying no, but in the nicest possible way."

---❖---

Losing It

A year later, it was football season. Trisha's dad smiled at his wife as he walked into the kitchen from the back door. He was a tall man. He wore an orange Longhorn sweatshirt and faded blue jeans. "The burgers are done. The one on top is medium-well, for Trisha."

Robin put her arm around him. "Chase, it was sweet of you to ask for Trisha's favorite meal. It's your celebration, after all."

"Jalapeño Swiss burgers with guacamole. T.J. and I like them, too, you know."

"The beans and potato salad are done. Pour me a beer, will you, while I go get the kids."

Robin wiped her hands on a dishtowel as she walked down the hall. She gave Trisha's door three knocks. "You there, Trisha? Dinner's ready."

When there was no response, she knocked again. After a moment she opened the door a crack. Trisha was lying on her back with her feet propped on the wall. Magazines covered the bed. Clothes littered the floor. She had an earphone in one ear and her cell phone next to the other. She giggled into the phone.

To make herself heard, Robin raised her voice. "Hey, Angel!"

Trisha gave her mom a quick sideways glance, frowned and continued talking into the cell phone.

"Trisha, we're celebrating your dad's promotion. Jalapeño Swiss burgers with guacamole, barbecue beans, and your favorite potato salad."

Trisha seemed not to hear any of this.

"Come on, Trisha, it's dinner time. We're waiting on you."

Trisha covered the mouthpiece. "I'm not hungry now. I'll get something later," she said and returned the phone to her ear.

"Trisha!"

"What?" Trisha squealed.

Robin stood there, waiting for Trisha to rise from her bed. When she realized she was being ignored, she felt the flush of anger and took three quick steps towards the bed.

"Give me that phone," she said, reaching for it.

Trisha turned away to keep her mother from taking the phone from her. "Hey!" she shouted and instinctively kicked at her mother's arm.

The blow struck her mother's stomach. As she fell backwards into the closet, she hit her head on a shoe rack. She shouted a curse as she tried to stand up.

Trisha screamed and ran from her room.

Robin ran after her. "Trisha Townsend, what on earth is wrong with you?" When she got to the end of the hall, she saw the open front door.

"Robin, what..." said Chase, but by then his wife had run out the front door.

Trisha's mother ran across the front lawn and into the street. In the distance, she saw her daughter running as fast as she could. Robin ran after her.

"Trisha, stop!" she shouted, running at full stride. "Come back here!"

By the time she reached the intersection at the end of the street, she was out of breath and could no longer see Trisha. She bent over, leaning on her knees. Out of the corner of her eyes, she noticed a neighbor taking plastic bags out of the back of a SUV. He had stopped to watch.

I must be quite a sight, she thought, and let out a laugh.

When Chase got to her, tears were streaming down her cheeks. "What's going on?"

All Robin could do was sob. Back in the house, she went to her bedroom and lay face down into her pillow, crying. "I lost it and my baby girl ran away."

Chase sat next to her and put his hand on her shoulder. "You lie here. I'll go make some calls. We'll find her."

When Trisha reached Aunt Maria's front door, she was out of breath and crying. She rang the doorbell. Her uncle Larry came to the door.

"Hey, Trish. What's this? Come inside. I'll get Maria."

"I need to use your bathroom," said Trisha.

Later, when Trisha walked into the hallway, Aunt Maria was standing there. She held out her arms. "Come here, Sweetheart."

Trisha hugged her aunt and began to cry again.

"Let's go sit on the back porch. I'll bring us some lemonade."

Maria sat down next to Trisha and handed her a glass. "I just called your dad to let him know you're here. Everything's okay. You don't need to call him back, and you can stay here as long as you want. All right?"

"Okay."

Maria looked up at the fading sunset, and the two of them sat in silence for a while.

"Aunt Maria?"

"What?"

"Why can't my mom and dad just let me have a life?"

"Why don't you tell me about it. What happened?"

"I was in my room talking on my phone with Ginger, my friend. Then Mom came in wanting me to eat, but I wasn't hungry. Then suddenly she rushed over to my bed and tried to grab my phone away from me. I was surprised and tried to push her away and she fell. I was scared so I ran out and she chased me down the street. It was crazy."

"Why do you think your mom was acting that way?"

"How should I know? I have a right to my life. I'm a good kid. I don't deserve to be treated like that."

"Like how?"

"Telling me when to eat and when not to eat. When I can talk to my friends. Going nuts and chasing me down the street."

"Trisha, try this. Imagine that you're the mother. You're making a special dinner. It's a celebration for your husband, you make all your daughter's favorite foods, just the way she likes them. You go to tell her it's time to eat and your daughter ignores you. You feel like she's dissing you."

Trisha thought about that. "I guess she got frustrated."

"Why do you suppose your mother lost her cool?"

"I don't know. She was on my case and wouldn't leave me alone."

They sat silently for a while as the evening darkened.

Then Aunt Maria said, "It sounds like cooler heads did not prevail. Sounds like everyone got upset and you took off."

"Yeah, that's about what happened, all right."

"You lost your cool, too, didn't you. Do you know why?"

"Aunt Maria, do we have to keep talking about this?"

"I promised you I'd be your coach, remember? Get you to think about why and what if?"

"Yeah."

"Okay, let's get to the point. These flare-ups don't happen very often, do they?"

"No."

"So when they do, you want to figure out why it happened, so you can handle it better the next time, right?"

"I guess so."

"So. Why did you blow your cool?"

"Because my mom was hassling me and I couldn't stand it."

"And you got angry."

"Aunt Maria, you don't have to live there. You don't know what it's like."

"You're right. And you know what? If I were your age and in that situation I probably would have reacted the same way. And the result would probably have been the same. So what were the consequences, Trisha?"

"Well, I'm here. With you."

"Right. And how about your parents? Everything cool there?"

"No, I guess not."

"That's right. Nobody's perfect, Sweetheart. Not you, and not your parents. Your mom probably expected you to come to dinner and be happy about what she did to please you. And when you acted indifferent, she became impatient. She probably felt hurt and got emotional and so you got emotional. This is what imperfect people do. But it causes hurt feelings. It damages relationships. Your parents are going to wonder if they can trust you."

"Trust me? For what?"

"Trisha, you're about to find out that whether your parents trust you is more important than you thought. You want to be more independent, but to give you that freedom, they have to trust you."

"What do you mean?"

"When is your curfew?"

"Curfew?"

"When are you required to be at home at night?"

"I'm supposed to be home for dinner."

"And what if your friends want to do something in the evening? When do you have to be back home?"

"By ten."

"But someday your friends may want to stay out later. You'd want your parents to allow it, right?"

"Sure."

"What would make them go along with it?"

"If it's like going to a movie or something, they should go along with it."

"That's reasonable, but what it comes down to is whether they trust you. If they trust you, they'll let you do it. If they don't, they won't. They want to be sure you'll do what you say you're going to do, that you'll be safe, that you'll stay out of trouble. They need to trust that you'll use good judgment."

"They should trust me. I'm a good kid."

"Yes, you are. But blowing your cool like you did earlier doesn't count in your favor. It makes them wonder. Later, when you get your driver's license, if they don't trust you to make good choices they won't give you the keys to the car. People get killed in cars all the time. They need to trust that you'll come home safe."

After a long silence, Trisha said, "What should I do now?"

"What would make them start trusting you again?"

"I don't know, I guess I overreacted. Maybe I should apologize."

"I think your mom overreacted, too. But you know what? I think you're right. Apologizing is a very adult thing to do. It's what a grown woman would do. Just take responsibility for what happened and tell them you're sorry. Tell them that in the future you'll be more thoughtful and consider their feelings."

"You think that would work?"

"I think it's a great start. Then you can just keep on doing the things that will cause them to trust you more."

"Like calling to let them know where I am."

"Right."

"You know, it's amazing to me that all this happened. It's crazy."

Aunt Maria nodded. "You're right. Nothing logical about it. Hey, while we're on the subject, why do you suppose you acted that way? You know, hot-headed instead of calm, cool and collected?"

"I don't know. I was just mad all of sudden."

"Like I've been telling you, the decision-making part of your brain is still under construction. It's hard to be logical when your brain is still programming itself for logic. It's a whole lot easier to just react emotionally."

"So what am I supposed to do?"

"Well, a really smart guy named Aristotle said that to get good at something, you have to do it a lot. So if you want to become a more logical person, you have to make yourself think logically. It's like tennis. To perfect your backhand stroke, you have to make yourself hit a lot of backhand shots, the right way."

"But if I get mad, how do I stay calm?"

"Good point. If keeping your cool were easy, everybody'd do it. But I have a few suggestions."

"What?"

"First, the next time you get steamed, it doesn't matter why, it could be something that happens at school. Or maybe you miss a shot on the tennis court. Or maybe your mom does something that gets on your nerves. The next time you feel mad, try this. Take three slow, deep breaths, and ask yourself this question – 'What's the most effective thing I can do right now?' Try that."

"Do you really think that'll work?"

"If you actually do it, yes, I think it will. For one thing, it'll keep you from reacting immediately. It'll give you a few seconds to calm down. And it'll cause you to use the logical part of your brain, the part that needs exercise right now. Maybe you'll think of something that will give you a good result. What happened tonight certainly wasn't a good result."

Maria looked into the distance as she took a sip from her glass of lemonade.

"The second thing you can do is to listen."

"Listen? Listen to what?"

"Remember the people skills ring of the onion?"

"Yeah."

"Listening is a people skill. I'm not just talking about being quiet so you can hear what your mom or dad says. I mean making sure you understand what they're trying to say. One reason everything flared up this evening was because neither you nor your mom did much listening."

"I heard what she said."

"But you didn't get what she meant, what she was trying to tell you. When you listen effectively you realize that somebody's trying to tell you something, even though they may not be communicating very well."

"So what was I supposed to do?"

"You ask yourself, what is she trying to say? When you think you know, check it with her. See if you understood it right."

"I don't get it."

"What you do is tell the other person what you think she meant, in your own words. I'll give you an example. Remember when your mom was telling you about dinner? You could have said, 'Mom, it sounds like you've been working on something special, and you want us to sit down together before it gets cold.' If you had said that, what do you think would have happened?"

"I guess she would have felt I heard her. But Aunt Maria, I can't imagine myself doing that. I was mad."

"That's right. It's a different way of reacting to someone. I didn't say this was easy. I said it's effective. But if you knew then what you know now, and if you could have forced yourself to do it, the conversation would have been a lot different. And what happened next would have been different."

"That's a big if, Aunt Maria."

"I know. It isn't easy when your habitual way of reacting is to do something else. It's not easy to hit a top spin when the tennis ball lands at your feet, either. You have to know what to do, and then practice it. So, do you know what to do next time?"

"Instead of popping off, I get quiet and calm down. Then I focus on what Mom is trying to say. Then I tell her what I think it is. Is that all there is to it?"

"Pretty much. Don't worry if you forget to do it or if it doesn't work well the first few times. Just don't give up. You wouldn't give up on your tennis game, so don't give up on communicating with your folks."

"Okay."

"You like those fancy burgers your dad makes, don't you?"

"Yeah."

"Well, they're easy to warm up. I'll take you home now so you can take care of business."

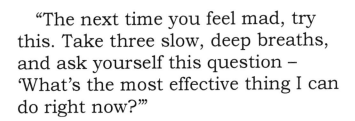

"The next time you feel mad, try this. Take three slow, deep breaths, and ask yourself this question – 'What's the most effective thing I can do right now?'"

"Whatever we learn to do, we learn by actually doing it: men come to be builders, for instance, by building, and harp players by playing the harp. In the same way, by doing just acts, we come to be just; by doing self-controlled acts, we come to be self-controlled; and by doing brave acts, we become brave."
- Aristotle, Greek philosopher (B.C. 384-322)

Mac Is Gone...

Robin opened the front door for Maria. They hugged, and Maria asked, "How's she doing?"

"She's really bummed out. She doesn't want to talk. She hasn't eaten much of anything for three days now. Mostly, she just naps. She's out back, lying on a beach towel."

"You think it would be okay if I talk to her?"

"Of course. But you know, I don't know if she'll want to talk much."

"Okay," said Maria. "I'll just go say hi."

It was a warm day in mid-April, and Trisha was lying on her stomach on an orange towel. She wore a bikini, and a bottle of sunscreen lay next to her. She appeared to be asleep. Aunt Maria brought a folding chair from the patio and sat down next to her. Trisha remained motionless, as if she were asleep. But after a few moments she turned her head and squinted at her aunt.

"Aunt Maria. Why are you here?"

"Well, Sweetheart, I heard about that business at your high school. I'm really sorry. I just wanted to check to see how you're doing."

"Mmm," said Trisha, and turned her head away.

Trisha said nothing for a long time. Her aunt broke the silence. "Would you like me to put some of this sunscreen on you?"

Trisha sat up. "No, I've been out here too long already. Let's go sit in the shade."

The two of them went to the patio.

"I'm sorry about your friend," said Maria. "I'm afraid I don't remember his name."

Tears formed in Trisha's eyes. "Mac. His name was Mac." She wiped her eyes and then said, "Actually, his name was Coker McCoy. But he hated the name Coker, so everybody called him Mac."

"How long did you know him?"

"A couple years. He was the bass player in Michael's band. He was a friend. Well, maybe not a friend, exactly, but I knew him. I hung out sometimes when they were practicing."

Trisha paused and then added, "Actually, he was kind of a jerk."

"What do you mean?"

"Oh, he was joking around all the time. He was so full of himself. He wasn't very nice to me. He didn't care much for people who couldn't play. He probably thought I was some kind of groupie or something. The nicest thing he ever did was offer me a drag on a marijuana cigarette."

"Oh my," said Maria. "Did you try it?"

"No."

"Why not?"

"You know I don't smoke, Aunt Maria. I'm an athlete. I know some of my friends are into alcohol and drugs and stuff. But they just want to be cool. I don't need any of that. Besides, I don't want to get high, and I'm afraid I'd get addicted or something. It's all craziness, Aunt Maria."

"Those are good instincts."

"Anyway, it gave him another reason to poke fun at me."

"But his death has affected you. You miss him?"

"I don't know. Sort of. It's hard to think of him as dead. One day he's jamming with the guys, having fun. He was supposed to graduate from high school in a few days. And now he's gone. He doesn't exist anymore."

The two of them sat in silence. It was springtime, and gusts of wind rolled in to shake the trees.

"He was a senior," said Trisha. "I don't know what he was planning to do. I just assumed he would stay with the band. Get gigs around Austin."

Maria nodded. "You never know how things will work out. Who knows where he would have ended up. I once knew a guy in college who was on special teams on the U.T. football team. I always thought of him as kind of an animal. But you know what happened to him? He made A's during his junior and senior years, and he went to med school. Now he's a big deal plastic surgeon out in L.A."

"Wow."

"So you never know. Mainly, people do what they care about and actions have consequences. Speaking of which, do you know the details about Mac's accident?"

Trisha sighed. "He was out with friends. He was kind of a rebel. He smoked, drank, used drugs, you name it. Anyway, the guys were drunk, and I guess he was speeding on the way home. He missed a curve and the car left the road and flipped over a couple times. No seat belt. That's pretty much it."

"I'm sorry. It's a tragedy when a young life is cut short like that. It reminds me of the toothpicks."

"What? Toothpicks?"

"Do you remember when I put ten toothpicks end to end on the table?"

"Oh yeah."

"The thing is, no one knows when their end will come or how long they'll live. Mac's life ended on the second toothpick. He made some bad choices and suffered terrible consequences."

"The funeral is Saturday."

"Are you going?"

"No, I've cried enough already. There was a memorial thing at school and everybody was upset. So that's it for me. I'm done."

Trisha knocked pieces of grass off her legs. "Aunt Maria?"

"Yes, Sweetheart?"

"What do you think happened to Mac? I know he's dead and all, but what about his soul? Is he in heaven now, or what?"

"To be honest, I don't know for sure."

"You go to church don't you, Aunt Maria?"

"Yes. Not every week, but Larry and I like going with my mom and dad. How about you?"

"Mom and Dad take us most Sundays. But to tell you the truth, I'm not sure that church is for me. It's boring. Most of the time I can't wait for it to be over."

"Well, you know you don't have to follow your parents' faith."

"I know."

"You can worship anywhere and any way you want. Or not at all. Have you given this any thought?"

"Not much. But lately I've been wondering."

"That maybe you should make a change?"

"I asked Mom about it and she said it's my choice. Whatever church I go to, or whether I go at all, it's my choice."

"There you go."

"But there are so many religions. It never occurred to me to check them out."

"Now that you're growing up, you may want to give some serious thought to life's big questions. Like, who am I? Why am I here? Where did all this come from? What happens to me when I die?"

"Where did you find your answers, Aunt Maria?"

"You know, I grew up going to church every Sunday, and my faith has always been a positive in my life. A lot of the people there were kind to me, helped me when I was a kid. There was a time after I left college that I got curious about other religions."

"What did you do?"

"I started reading, looking for answers. It was like being on a path of learning. One thing I found out is that most of what's going on here on Earth and in the universe is still a mystery. For example, scientists aren't really sure what gravity is. And after hundreds of years of research, they still don't know what light is. There are theories, but the theories keep changing. They embrace theories when the evidence makes sense, even when they aren't totally sure. They accept these theories on faith. You know what I mean by faith?"

"You mean they believe?"

"Right. They take it on faith, until better evidence comes along. And that's what I do, I guess. I try to find out what makes sense for me, then I say, 'This is what I believe.' When it comes to religion, I take a lot of things on faith. I guess I've come full circle. I still like that old church and the people in it. They're almost like family. Most of all, I believe that if I live a good life and treat people right, I'll be fine. My faith plays a big part in that."

Trisha looked at her aunt without saying anything.

Aunt Maria kept talking. "I was visiting with a young woman last week. She was in her mid-twenties. She had a miserable childhood. Count your blessings, Trisha. Not everyone has nice parents. I won't go into it. It's a tragic story. Anyway, the bottom line is, she's fine today. She told me that what got her through was the time she spent with her grandparents. And going to church. The people there helped her. It was a good place for her to retreat to. It gave her hope."

"I'm glad it worked for her, but that doesn't mean it'll work for me."

"Spirituality is a personal thing. It's amazing how many paths there are, and they're all different. Whatever you decide has to work for you. So you see, only you can make that choice."

"I know."

"But to get your own answers, you have to pursue them. Until you resolve these questions for yourself, it'll be like drifting on the ocean. You need to find your solid ground."

Trisha gazed at the noon sky.

"But to get back to your original question, I know some people who would say Mac's soul is in heaven now. Others would say no, it's in some kind of limbo. Others reserve judgment, saying that God works in mysterious ways. Some even believe that people don't have souls. It's a matter of faith, what you choose to believe. The bottom line is, your friend is gone, and you have to make your peace with that and move on. And doing that isn't always so easy. I think the best way to get through it is to go ahead and feel sad. Then over time you'll get used to his absence, and remember the good things. And they'll make you smile. It's what happens when we lose someone we know. Down the road, the band will get a new bass player."

"Huh. Maybe."

The two of them sat in silence for a while. Then Maria said, "Trisha, I'm doing something next week that might help take your mind off all this. It's a fundraiser event called Relay for Life. I'm on the board, so I get involved every year. You want to come along?"

"What is it?"

"It's for the American Cancer Society. They have Relay for Life events all over the U.S. Ours will be held at the high school, on the track. Groups organize relay teams to walk laps on the track all night long. They compete to raise the most money. There's entertainment, food, and special ceremonies, like a huge display of luminaria candles. Actually, it's a lot of fun and a good cause, and I'd love for you to come help."

"Really? What would I do?"

"I'm sure we need volunteers to work the stage Saturday night. I think it would be an uplifting experience. Would you like to come with me and help out?"

Trisha considered this for a moment, then she said, "Okay. Count me in."

"Spirituality is a personal thing. It's amazing how many paths there are, and they're all different. Whatever you decide has to work for you. So you see, only you can make that choice."

Relay for Life

Trisha didn't go to the Relay for Life with her aunt. She was still having heavy thoughts, and she didn't think a cancer fund-raising event would cheer her up.

But the following year her aunt invited her again, and this time Trisha was curious.

It was near the end of April, and they arrived at the football stadium late in the afternoon. Trisha saw hundreds of people strolling around the track, checking out the booths and displays.

"This thing goes all night, so we've got plenty of time to do what we need to do," said Aunt Maria. "Let's go check out some of the booths."

They approached a booth with a tropical theme. A big sign said, "Margaritaville," and Jimmy Buffet music was playing in the background. Young people wore sunglasses and tropical shirts and sat in deck chairs. The booth sold a variety of fruit-flavored smoothies.

"High school kids," said her aunt. "The idea is to raise money for cancer and have fun doing it. Every team raised money to qualify, and some are raising more by selling food, drinks and other items. At the same time, each team keeps one person walking around the track at all times. That's why they call it a relay. It's an affirmation of how people support each other

83

and about not giving up, even when you're tired. They take turns walking through the night, and someone is still walking when the sun comes up."

Trisha looked around her. There were more than twenty booths, with tents pitched in the grass behind them.

The next booth was manned by a dentist's office. Behind an enormous tooth was a sign that said, "No pain, no gain." They had a grill fired up for hamburgers.

"The relay committee gives awards to the team with the most creative booth, the team that raises the most money, and so forth. Most teams take the competition seriously and plan for months. Bragging rights."

Trisha laughed.

"I tell you what. I need to find the coordinator. I'm on the judging committee, so I need to know when they're going to start. Why don't you go over to the stage and see what they'd like you to do?"

"Okay."

The stage was set up behind the north end zone. Trisha found a man in a jump suit carrying chairs up the back steps.

"Are you in charge of the stage?" asked Trisha.

"Are you my helper? They said I might have some help this year."

"Yes. My name is Trisha."

"I'm Doug. Glad to see you. The kick-off is the Survivor Lap. They're waiting on me to get the sound system working. If you'll bring the chairs and equipment up to the stage I can get started on the sound."

"Okay."

After Trisha got the speakers and other equipment on the stage, she and Doug adjusted the amplifier and mixer. As they tested the microphones, a woman came up to the stage.

"Hi, I'm Judy. We're ready to start. You got a mic for me? I need it down on the track."

Doug set her up, and she started making announcements. "Ladies and gentlemen, we're about to kick off this year's Relay for Life! According to tradition, we begin each Relay with a Survivor Lap. If you're a survivor, please check in and get your yellow t-shirt and assemble on the track at the Start Line, west of the stage."

Trisha hadn't noticed that some of the Relay t-shirts were white and some were yellow. People began to gather behind the stage.

As Trisha made her way into the crowd, she heard the woman giving instructions. "We need all the survivors behind the stage now, please. We'll begin the Survivor Lap in five minutes."

Trisha found herself surrounded by people in yellow t-shirts. All these people had had cancer. She was surprised to see so many young people. A mother guided a stroller with a toddler in a yellow t-shirt. A woman in white pushed an older man in a wheel chair.

"All right, all you beautiful people! You're all survivors. You never gave up. Today we honor and celebrate you. We celebrate your life!"

The crowd cheered, and she continued. "As you walk by the mic, please say your name, the kind of cancer you had and how long you've been a survivor. Then you and your loved ones can walk the first lap together."

She handed the mic to a young woman. "I'm Doris Daniels. Colon cancer. Six and a half years." The crowd cheered and she walked on to the track.

An elderly man announced: "My name is Tim Jeffers. Prostate cancer. Sixteen years."

One after another, survivors proudly announced their victory.

A woman with a scarf over her bald head approached. "I'm Becky. Breast cancer. Eight months."

"I'm here with my boy, Charles Brewer. Brain cancer. Three months, and he's going to beat it."

"I'm Hunter Belanus. I had lung cancer but I've been free for four years."

Trisha felt a lump in her throat, and tears filled her eyes. She looked around at these people who had faced death. Many of them also had tears in their eyes.

One by one, people took the microphone and began their lap. This continued for half an hour, until the last person had spoken and the track was a river of yellow shirts.

Later, Trisha helped a musician set up the stage for his performance. His white hair flowed from under his black cowboy hat. He tested the sound and then spoke to the crowd.

"Welcome y'all to the Relay for Life. My name is Ronny Faith, and thank you for asking me back. People I love have been touched by cancer. Some survived. Some did not. So here's a ballad I wrote for last year's Relay. It's called 'Stand Up.'"

Trisha liked his deep voice, his Texas drawl, and the lyrics of his song. His next piece was more lively, a humorous story about not giving up on love. She enjoyed the way he played the guitar. Maybe someday she could play like that.

After his set, Trisha followed him to one of the team booths, where he was buying a soft drink. "Mr. Faith?"

He turned to look at her and smiled. "That's me," he said. "But you can call me Ronny."

"Ronny, I'm Trisha," she said and held out her hand.

"A pleasure. What can I do for you?"

"I just wanted to say I love your music, the way you play that guitar. Did you write all those songs?"

"Yeah, they're mine. Thanks, I'm glad you like 'em."

"Do you have a few minutes? I'd like to ask about your music."

"Matter of fact, I have more than a few minutes. I don't do my final set until nine." He looked around. "Why don't we sit down over here in the bleachers? Can I get you something to drink?"

"No thanks. I just had something."

They climbed to the third row and Ronny laid his guitar next to him.

"Now. What do you want to know?"

"How did you get started?"

"Oh, I was about ten years old. My daddy was killed right in front of me. My momma couldn't deal with it and took off, and I had to live with my aunt and uncle. Pretty soon I was in the church choir. A guy there saw me fooling around with his guitar, and he showed me how to play."

"You took lessons from him?"

"I wouldn't call it lessons. He showed me some things and told me to go practice. I pretty much taught myself. I'd just listen to records and try to do what the artist was doing. I stayed with it and eventually hooked up with a band."

"I'm learning the guitar," said Trisha.

"Are you now? How long have you been at it?"

"About three years. My dad got me started and friends showed me things, but now I'm learning from a teacher. Dad lets me learn on his old guitar, but I'm hoping to buy a new one soon. I've been saving up. Yours is beautiful. Would you tell me about it? Do you think one like that would work for me?"

"Well, that depends on what kind of music you want to play. Folk? Rock? Country? Classical? Jazz?"

"To be honest, I like your kind of music. What would you call it? Country rock?"

"I don't call it nothin', Trisha. If I like it, I play it. So tell me. How serious are you about playing the guitar?"

"I take lessons twice a week. I'm a sophomore in high school, and if I'm not studying or playing tennis, I'm playing the guitar."

"Is your dad a musician, too?"

"No. He learned to play when he was in college, but then he gave it up. It's pretty much my guitar now, until I get a new one."

"Buying a guitar is like getting married. You buy it to have and to hold until death do you part. That's why you need to know what kind of music you want to play."

"I really love the way you play. I hope I can play that well someday."

"Well, Trisha, you can play like me if you want to. Even better. A whole lot of people play the guitar better than me. It's just learning the techniques and practicing. Anybody can show you what to do, but it needs to become second nature. You said you're a tennis player. It's like that. Practice, practice, and more practice until it feels natural. Then it's just feelin' and pickin'. No thinkin'. So let's run the numbers here. How often do you practice each week?"

"About six days a week."

"And on average how many hours each day?"

"About two hours."

"Okay, let's see here. Six times two is twelve hours a week. Call it fifteen. Say fifty weeks a year, that's 750 hours a year. Times three years, that's more than 2,000 hours. That's a lot of hours, but you know what they say?"

"No, what?"

"They say to be a top performer in anything, you need to put in at least 10,000 hours of practice. You can be a pretty fair guitar player with less, but the best pay those kind of dues."

"I guess you'd call me a beginner, then," she said.

"Everybody starts out as a beginner. The ones with the passion stay with it. There's a lot to learn. You stay with it, and you'll learn it. I guarantee it."

"Can you tell me about being a professional musician?"

"You know, there's no one way to do it. Just people doing what they like to do. Some want to play in a group. I'm solo today because I'm helping the Relay for Life. Something I believe in. My wife's an eleven-year breast cancer survivor, and I've been doing this gig for the past five years. My band is called Quickwater. When I'm not playing with them, I write mystery novels. And when I'm not doing that, I help my sister with her gallery in Wimberley."

"Cool."

"Some like playing in bars and places like that. Some go on the road. Some like recording. Some teach. Some play just for the love it, performing for charities and stuff like that. Some people just write. I know a few guys who have great voices but hate leaving home, so they do demos."

"What's a demo?"

"When you write a song you want somebody to publish it. But they want to hear it first to see if they like it, so you need to record it. That's what they call a demo. If a writer isn't a great singer, he might hire somebody to sing it for him. Then, if you get real lucky a star will hear it and want to cover it. If it's a hit, there's some money."

"I think I like writing."

"Really? Do you have some songs?"

"I have a few."

"Do you sing?"

"Yeah, I like singing."

"Well, all right," he said and reached for his guitar. "Play one for me."

"What? Now?"

"We got time. It's just you and me, nothing to get stage fright about."

"I guess I can play something. You really want to hear me sing?"

"I really do. If you're willing."

"Okay." She strummed a few chords. "Wow, this is a nice guitar. Do you mind if I stand?"

"Go for it."

"Okay. It's called 'I Like It Cause I Like It.'"

"All right!" said Ronny with an encouraging smile.

Trisha played some lead-in chords. Her body came alive as she sang:

> *I like laughin' with my friends and days that never end,*
> *Girly talks and wanderin' walks.*
> *I like sunny days and starry nights,*
> *Cruisin' back roads with no place to go.*
> *I like holdin' hands and country rock bands,*
> *Strummin' my guitar and singin' my song.*
> *I like cowgirl boots and cowgirl jeans,*
> *Dancin' on Friday nights and all the bright lights.*
>
> *You can like what you want*
> *'Cause you gotta be you*
> *But I gotta be me*
> *So stay outta my face,*
> *I like it 'cause I like it.*

"Like that," she said

Ronny clapped. "Hoo! All right now! You got something good going on there, girl."

Trisha smiled and handed the guitar back to Ronny. "I'm glad you liked it."

"Trisha you've got a good voice, you know that? It's a down-to-earth husky sound. Sort of reminds me of Wanda Jackson, only with a kind of sweetness."

"Wanda Jackson?"

"She was a huge rockabilly star back in the fifties. Kind of a female Elvis Presley. Kid, that's a good song. A lot of people will identify with it. You need to get that one published."

"How would I do that?"

"I can show you. You know what? I'd like you to meet the guys in my group. We jam on Tuesdays at Mona's."

"I don't know if I'm good enough to play with them."

"Well, this is a good time to start. You gotta play around with music. Jamming will teach you things and build your confidence. Besides, we want to try working with a female singer. Might be interesting." He handed her his card. "Call me to make sure we're getting together."

Trisha could feel her heart beating. "I will."

"Okay. Time for me to get back. It was a pleasure meeting you, Trisha."

"Me, too. Thanks."

When she got back to the stage, a woman was leading the crowd in yoga exercises. Later, Ronny returned to do another set. When he was done, she went over to him to shake his hand.

"That was great. I loved it."

"Thanks. This is a good crowd."

"Thanks for inviting me to come play with you sometime. I will definitely call you."

He waved as he left. "I hope you do! You take care now."

Later, Aunt Maria came to the stage. "Hi, Trisha, are you having fun yet?"

"I've been helping Doug set up for the acts and hanging around in case there's a problem. Oh, Aunt Maria, something great happened."

"Really? What?"

"I met the singer who played earlier. He talked to me about his music and I played a little for him and he invited me to jam with his group sometime."

"Are you going to?"

"I think it will be a good challenge for me."

"Tell your mom and dad about it. They might want to meet him."

"Sure, that would be good."

"Oh look, Trisha. They're starting to light the luminarias." She pointed to the bleachers.

"What's a luminaria?"

"It's a candle mounted in some sand inside a paper bag. We sell them to people who write a dedication on the bag. Then they light them all at once after sunset."

Trisha looked at the bleachers. The stadium lights went off and the sky was dark overhead. In the bleachers, rising row upon row, tiny lights merged into a flickering display of the word HOPE.

Aunt Maria's voice was soft. "I dedicated a bag to my friend Sherry who died from lung cancer last year."

Trisha thought about the people in the yellow shirts. Hope had to be a big part of surviving. Her eyes filled with tears again.

"You know the real reason I do this, Trisha?"

"No, why?"

"You've heard the phrase, 'give back?'"

"Sure."

"Well, you can't always give back to the people who helped you when you needed it. So you give back to the world. There are times when people need a helping hand. I like Relay for Life because it lets me do what I do best, which is to organize things. And people are going to be helped in a big way. Our goal this year is to net a hundred thousand dollars. The American Cancer Society uses the money for research, education and services that help people cope with treatment. There are thousands of Relay for Life events going on around the country this time of year."

"Wow."

"Doing this is good for me. I'm involved in something larger than myself. It makes me feel like I'm the kind of woman who helps people." She smiled at Trisha. "And so are you, Sweetheart. Today you stepped up. You gave back."

"I really liked being here," said Trisha.

"I've met a lot of people through Relay, people who are now friends and people who help me in my business. And you met someone who might help you with your music!"

Trisha smiled back at her aunt. "I guess I did. Aunt Maria, have you ever had to struggle?"

"Of course. Everyone has their share of bad times. Larry's dad died of prostate cancer, you know."

Maria was silent for a while. "I was laid off once, many years ago. My bank was sold to a bigger bank and they eliminated my job. It was hard to find a new one. I had to work part-time as a bookkeeper for a while."

"I didn't know that."

"In an odd way it turned out to be a good thing. I learned about business from the customer's perspective. I learned about service and how to deal with people. I ended up doing bookkeeping work for a regional bank, and later they hired me full-time. They say when life dishes up lemons you need to make lemonade, and for a while there that's what I was doing. Trisha, sooner or later we all need help. So when we contribute like this, we make things better. And we're stronger for it."

"I guess so."

"Like everything else, how you contribute will be up to you. It could be a worthy cause some of your friends are involved in, or you could start something new, something you care about."

"Maybe it would involve my music."

"That's a good idea. Something worth thinking about."

"Yeah. I've got a lot I need to think about."

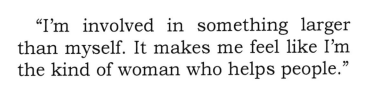

"I'm involved in something larger than myself. It makes me feel like I'm the kind of woman who helps people."

One of the Girls

Maria's doorbell rang. When she opened the door, Trisha was standing there with her tennis bag. Sometimes on Saturdays Trisha played with her aunt to stay in shape during the tennis team's off-season.

Maria gave her a hug. "You ready to whip me?"

"I don't feel like whipping anybody today."

She gave her niece a look. "What gives?"

"You got any coffee?"

"Sure. Come on in and let's have some."

The two of them sat in the kitchen and silently sipped at their cups. After a while, Maria said, "It's nice just sitting here and drinking our coffee in peace. But you don't seem your usual self."

"Aunt Maria...." Trisha paused.

"Yes, dear?"

"I screwed up."

"What happened?"

"I did something stupid last night. There was no harm done, but...."

Maria waited for her to finish her sentence.

"I don't feel good. I think I have a hangover."

"You were out drinking last night?"

"I wouldn't put it that way."

"Why don't you tell me what happened."

Trisha took another sip of coffee. "Our football team won last night, and some of my friends wanted to celebrate, so we went over to my friend Anita's house. We were having cokes and raiding her refrigerator. Then Anita said a little rum with coke makes a great drink. Everyone wanted to try it. It tasted pretty good, so I had another. And then another. After a while my head felt weird, and I got worried. I thought I was drunk. I probably was a little drunk. So I asked Lacy to drive me home. But she'd been drinking, too, so we had to be real careful. I went straight to bed. But now I feel like crap."

"I'm glad you're okay. It's a good thing you came home when you did, but maybe you should have called your mom and dad or a cab."

"I guess, but I didn't want them to know. And I didn't think of a cab until we were almost to my house."

"I agree you made a mistake. I'm not going to lecture you about it, but it would be good to learn from it. Can we talk about it a little?"

"I guess so, if I can have some more coffee."

"No problem. I'd just like to ask a few questions."

Maria topped off both their cups.

"I understand that it's natural to be curious about alcohol and to want to experiment. But aside from the fact that you aren't old enough, why did you continue drinking?"

"I don't know, Aunt Maria. Everyone was doing it. We were having fun, and I didn't know it would make me woozy."

"You've never been drunk before, have you?"

"No."

"So you didn't know what three drinks would do to you."

"No. It sort of took me by surprise."

"Well, now you know what it feels like."

"I didn't like it. I didn't like feeling dizzy and not being my normal self."

"Then what happened?"

"Well we all started saying silly things and giggling a lot. That was kind of fun. But after a while I realized something was happening to me. I thought maybe I'd gone too far and I sort of panicked and wanted to go home."

"So what happened?"

"Like I said, Lacy drove me home, and nothing happened. But I was worried that something might have happened."

"Like what?"

"If the cops had noticed Lacy's driving and stopped us, that would have been awful. I never would have heard the end of it."

"Lacy was having trouble driving?"

"I guess she was doing okay. We were both concentrating. I guess she got home okay."

"You aren't sure?"

"I haven't heard anything. I just figured she made it and slept in."

"If she had an accident, I guess you would have heard about it."

"I guess."

"I assume your mom and dad don't know about this."

"Oh god, no."

"Well, your secret is safe with me."

"Thanks, Aunt Maria."

"But do you mind if I ask a couple more questions?"

"Okay."

"You know, you're such a strong-willed, independent person, I'm surprised you gave in to what the other girls wanted to do. Why didn't you excuse yourself and just tell them straight coke was fine with you?"

"I was curious and it seemed harmless to celebrate and have a little fun with my friends."

"So you went with fun and friendship and didn't think about the consequences."

"Yeah, I didn't think it through at the time."

"How about next time?"

"Next time?"

"You know, the next time your friends want to include you in some fun and excitement. What will you do?"

"Not everything that's fun and exciting is bad, Aunt Maria."

"That's true. And you seem to have learned your lesson about rum and coke, but what about other stuff? What if they want to smoke marijuana? Or steal something? Kids get ideas for fun on the spur of the moment. What if your friends want to pull a prank on somebody?"

"I'm not interested in any of that, Aunt Maria."

"I know, but you didn't want to get buzzed, and it happened anyway. How will you avoid future trouble?"

"It's like you've told me before. I need to think about the consequences. I guess what I learned is that it's not so easy. I have to remember to ask myself what if and think of the possible consequences."

"That's a good plan. Keep trying. If you do, I guarantee it'll get easier."

"I hope so."

"And I want to give you something you can use when your friends pressure you to do something you don't want to do. An out."

"An out? What do you mean?"

"I mean you should feel free to use your parents, or even me as an excuse. All you have to do is say something like, 'This sounds like fun, but I've got two strikes against me right now and if my dad got wind of this it would be really, really bad for me. You all have fun, but count me out on this one.' It's an escape out."

"I see. That might work."

"As for alcohol, after you're 21 you can choose whether you want to drink. And if you do, you can decide to drink responsibly."

"I've heard that about this 'drink responsibly' business. What does it mean?"

"It means limiting how much you drink. Pacing yourself. Having one drink and waiting an hour or so for your system to deal with it before you have another."

"I see."

"The problem is that having one drink can get you in the mood for another. That's when it starts to affect your judgment. Having several drinks can inhibit your thinking until doing something crazy seems like the perfect thing to do."

"And I might forget to think about what could happen."

"It's partly because of the alcohol and partly because teenagers have to work harder to use the decision-making part of their brain. If they get a buzz on, they might decide to do something like getting in a car and bombing around town. If they're caught, they'll be charged with DUI. There could be big fines. They could lose their licenses. And the insurance company could triple or quadruple the price of their car insurance. Worse things could happen."

"Like a car accident."

"Exactly. Alcohol not only impairs your judgment, it slows your reactions. It makes it easier to lose control or run into another car. People could die, Trisha—innocent people."

They were silent for a moment, and then Trisha said softly, "I see now how easy it is to drink too much. One of my dad's friends is an alcoholic. Dad says he's mean when he drinks."

"It can be hard on relationships. And it can be hard on the body. Your body sees alcohol as a poison and has to work hard to get rid of it."

"Yeah, I know."

"To me, the worst thing about teenagers drinking is what alcohol can do to your brain. And I'm not talking about killing off a few hundred brain cells."

"What do you mean?"

"It's the same consequence as when mothers smoke or drink during pregnancy. The danger is that the substance could disrupt the baby's normal development during a sensitive growth period, causing a defect in the baby's body or brain."

"Mom told me about that."

"Most people don't know that during the teen years, the front part of their brain is in a similar sensitive growth period, as you and I have talked about. So the danger is similar, that drinking could disrupt a teen's normal brain development, causing a defect in the part of the brain that does higher-level thinking. The damage could be permanent."

"I never thought about that. Aunt Maria, alcohol isn't a big deal for me like it is for some of my friends. I try to stay away from it."

"I know you do. But let me ask you this. What if your friends want to do something you know is risky? Would you go along, take a chance so you could be accepted by the cool crowd? If you didn't, they might think you're some kind of prude or party pooper."

"My friends aren't like that."

"You must be hanging out with the right friends. What if someday you find yourself in a group that gets a crazy idea to do something you don't feel right about? What will you do then?"

"Aunt Maria, I know people do stupid things sometimes. That's not me. I'd just say, 'You girls go ahead. I have something else I have to do.'"

"And if they try to talk you into it? If they kid you or say mean things to you?"

"Then they're not my friends."

"You got that right. But peer pressure can be tough. People want to be liked and have other kids think they're cool. Some want to be popular so much that they'll go along with whatever the cool crowd is doing. Dress a certain way. Act a certain way. Do what everyone else is doing, even if it's stupid. Or illegal. Or even dangerous. And then later, when things go bad, they wonder what they were thinking about."

"Maybe they weren't thinking. Just having fun."

"Exactly. I'm glad you're wise enough to know that if you don't think about the consequences, you could end up doing something you regret for the rest of your life."

"I'm really trying, Aunt Maria."

"I know you are."

They had a few more sips of coffee and Maria said, "So hey, you seem more perky now. You want to try beating me at tennis now?"

"Okay. But you have to promise not to go easy on me."

"Do I ever?"

"No. Thanks, Aunt Maria."

❖

"Peer pressure can be tough for a teenager. Kids want to be liked. They want other kids to think they're cool. They might want to be popular so much that they'd go along with whatever the cool crowd is doing. Dress a certain way. Act a certain way. Do what they do, even if it's stupid. Or illegal. Or even dangerous. And then later, when things go bad, they wonder what they were thinking about."

❖

"The problem is that having one drink can get you in the mood for another. That's when it starts to affect your thinking. Having several drinks can make you think that doing something crazy is the perfect thing to do."

❖

The Gruene Hall Gig

A year later, Trisha and her family were walking down the main street of Gruene, Texas. It was a Friday night and hundreds of people crowded the sidewalks.

"Look at all those motorcycles parked outside that store. Cotton-Eyed Joe's. I wonder what's going on there," her mother said.

"For a small town they seem to have a lot going on. You suppose it's the Guadalupe River tubing crowd?" her dad asked.

T.J. pointed straight ahead. "There it is. Gruene Hall."

The plain, weathered one-story wooden building stood in the shadow of the Gruene water tower. They could hear the squeak of rusty springs as patrons entered through the old screen doors.

"It doesn't look like much. Needs a paint job," said T.J.

They crossed the street. "Ronny says it's the oldest continuously operating dance hall in Texas," Trisha said. "All kinds of country music legends got their start here. George Strait, Willy Nelson, Jerry Jeff Walker, Delbert McClinton, Hank Williams, Jr., and a bunch of others. He said most of them still come back."

"Willy Nelson," said her dad. "Hank Williams. Impressive."

As they approached the hall, Trisha saw a sign written in chalk: "NO COVER. Ronny Faith and Quicksand."

She opened the old screen door and peered inside. The stand-up bar was crowded with people holding bottles of beer. One wall was covered with framed photographs of entertainers.

They walked along the wall until they entered a long room. Trisha looked around. The place looked like an old barn filled with picnic tables and wooden benches along the wall. Old wooden signs lined the walls. One said, "Orange Crush – Made from fresh oranges." Another said, "Ed Moeller's Café, open all night. Where everybody meets everybody." Beyond the picnic tables were some pool tables. The wide-plank wooden floor creaked under their feet as they settled at an empty table up front.

"Cool," said T.J. "These tables have a gazillion initials carved in them." He rubbed his fingers on a carving in front of him that read, "Dale 6-15-59."

Ronny was up front with the band. As they finished setting up, Trisha walked over.

"Hey, Ronny!"

He turned around and smiled. "Hey, Trisha."

"Everything okay?"

"Couldn't be better. Who'd you come with?"

"I brought my whole family. They can make a lot of noise. Why don't you come over and say hi after the set?"

"I will."

"You know, this is only the second time I've been to one of your gigs. Gruene Hall, man. I'm excited."

"Performing in front of a crowd is always exciting. Every time."

"Great! Well, knock 'em dead!" said Trisha, and she returned to her family. Aunt Maria and Uncle Larry had joined her mother and father.

Her younger brother, T.J., now fifteen, had only recently discovered Texas country music. "Which one is Ronny?"

"He's the one with the silver pony tail. He's the lead singer. The guy at the keyboard, that's Jones. The guy in the vest is Santana. He plays bass guitar. The drummer is Emilio."

A vocal Friday night crowd had filled the room. Families, young couples, older couples, locals, bikers, tourists—all country music lovers. Some wore jeans, western hats and boots. Others wore t-shirts and shorts. People stood at the back of the room.

And then, without any introduction, the band launched into a song. The first notes boomed and vibrated off the walls. The crowd leaned forward and moved with the music as it washed over them. A syncopated beat drove a high-energy song about reckless men looking for excitement. Ronny and Santana sang the chorus in harmony:

So me and my boys
We were haulin' on our Harleys,
Me and my boys
We had money in our pockets,
Me and my boys
We were Bandera bound,

Honky-tonk crazy on a Saturday night.

As the last note of the song echoed across the hall, applause rose to meet it. Trisha and her family cheered. Trisha shouted to her aunt, "Didn't I tell you they were good?"

When the cheering subsided, Ronny said. "Y'all are great. Thank you. You know, I've written a couple hundred songs, and I have to tell you I have no idea where they come from. Out of left field, I guess. Last week we were trying out some new stuff, and this song came to me. The group liked it so we decided we'd play it tonight. First time anywhere, just for you, here's 'Don't Take Nothin' for Granted.'"

The first few chords were slow and mournful, and Ronny began:

> *I once had the love of a beautiful woman.*
> *She was there every day, she was there every night.*
> *When I came home late she didn't ask me no questions,*
> *She just loved me so good and she treated me right.*

Trisha noticed that people were nodding their heads to the music, as if they were remembering their own heartaches. The group followed with songs about football, failure, and loneliness. It was Texas life set to music, and the crowd loved it.

At the end of the set, Ronny signed CDs and talked with fans. Then he came over to greet Trisha's family. He shook hands with everyone. "I remember meeting you, Mrs. Townsend, when you brought Trisha over the first time. Mr. Townsend, glad to meet you. Is this your brother, Trisha?"

"I'm T.J."

"I hope you're enjoying the music."

"It's wonderful," Aunt Maria told him.

"Thank you! This is a good crowd. We appreciate your support." He turned to Trisha. "Say, there's something you could do for me."

"Sure, name it."

"How about coming up and doing one of your songs to lead off the next set."

"What? Are you kidding?"

"No, man. I told you someday you'd play a gig with us. Well, this is it."

"I don't know. I mean, I'm not prepared."

"Hey, this crowd will love you. You've played with us a lot. It'll be just like that. We'll do that one song the band likes. They're the ones who suggested it. Now come on, let's play some music."

Trisha took a quick look at the people around her. They were laughing and having a good time. She hadn't expected this. She could make a fool of herself. But how could she say no when he'd helped her so much? A voice in her head said, *Gruene Hall. You could be on stage at Gruene Hall.*

"Okay. Do you have a guitar for me?"

Ronny grinned. "We always bring several, just in case."

She took a deep breath and walked to the front. Santana grinned and raised his palm for a high five. When she slapped it, the muscles in her body relaxed. *Just me and the guys.*

"Can we do 'Getting Ready to Fly?'" she asked the band.

"Know it well," said Jones, and he zipped through a few chords.

Trisha picked up the guitar and plugged in the pickup. She had used this instrument before. She looked out at the crowd. People were returning to their seats. She gave Ronny a nod.

"Let's have some fun," Ronny said. Then he leaned into the mic: "Y'all ready for more good times?"

Whistles and clapping sounded around the hall.

"To lead off this set, we've got something really special for you. We've been working with a young singer-songwriter this past year. She's a special talent. She's here tonight to hear us perform, and she agreed to do a song with us. You're gonna love her, so give your best Texas shout for Trisha Townsend!"

When the cheers and clapping subsided, Trisha spoke into the mic. "Every time I sing this song, I think of my mom. She says I'm like a bird getting ready to leave the nest. My mom and her sister, Maria, are the most important women in my life. So this song is for you two," she said, pointing at them.

The band played a stanza, and then Trisha's sweet, husky voice filled the hall. It was a high-energy rockabilly song, and she sang it with her whole body, as if she were dancing.

> *In this crazy crazy world*
> *You gotta go it all alone.*
> *You got people who will love you,*
> *But you go it all alone.*

I been livin' I been lovin',
I been tryin' to fly higher,
But I need more livin'
And I need more lovin',
Need to spread my wings
'Cause I'm gonna fly higher.

I jus' wanna be me,
I don't wanna be you.
I jus' gotta be free,
Not gonna be blue.
I got a long way to go,
But I'm already goin',
I'm gettin' ready to fly,
Yeah, I'm gettin' ready to fly.

Ronny played a solo riff, then Trisha came in again.

Oh I see the big lights,
They make me warm all over.
You know they shine so bright,
They make me light as a feather.
I can feel it in my heart,
And I feel it in my toes.
Gotta listen to my heart,
Gotta listen to my soul.
Gotta sing another song
'Cause I'm ready to go.

'Cause I wanna be me
I don't wanna be you.
I jus' gotta be free,
Not gonna be blue.
I got a long way to go,
But I'm already goin',

I'm gettin' ready to fly,
Yeah, I'm gettin' ready to fly.

Jones came in with a keyboard riff, Trisha sang a final verse, and the band ended strong with the chorus. The crowd cheered, She blew a kiss to the audience, bowed and returned to her seat.

Her mother had tears in her eyes. "Oh, Honey, you were amazing."

Her father beamed. T.J. looked at Trisha as if he'd never seen her before. "That rocked, Big Sister."

Maria hugged her tight. As the band began to play again, Maria leaned over to speak into Trisha's ear. "You're quite the woman now."

"I don't feel like a woman. I feel like a kid."

"Of course you do. But you handle yourself with a lot of maturity. Like your song says, you're ready to fly."

After the second set, Trisha's family said goodbye to the band and went to a nearby restaurant for dessert.

Her brother was still excited from hearing his sister sing on stage. "That was so cool, Trisha. You're like the real deal. Are you going to do more concerts? You could be a star."

"I'm glad you liked it. I'm not sure what I'm going to do or if I want to go down that road. The music is so much fun, but there are thousands of people just like me out there, all desperate to make it, and only a few do. Most singers are like Ronny and his band, guys with real talent who have to scramble for gigs and sell CDs to the crowd. I don't know if I want that kind of life."

Conversation shifted from music to what they were planning to do that weekend. When they were done, Maria took Trisha aside. "Your parents are really proud of you."

"I give you credit, too, Aunt Maria. You helped me get on track. I still take that stuff about personal strength and people skills and critical thinking seriously. I have a lot to learn."

"We never stop learning, Trisha. But you have a head start. You could have blown off the hard work, but you didn't. You took it seriously. Now you can use your senior year to prepare for college. Are you going to continue working on your music?"

"I like it. I get little gigs here and there, and there might be more. That and my pet-sitting business is helping me save for college."

"Have you decided what you want to do? What you want to major in?"

"I'm not sure. My grades are good, and I've been thinking it might be science or premed. I like the idea of helping people."

"There are some good careers out there that will let you do that."

"I know. My chemistry teacher, Mrs. Fleming, has been telling me about it."

"Your life isn't all work, is it? Are you dating anyone special?"

Trisha laughed. "Not really. I have a few guy friends, and sometimes we do stuff. But the truth is, I don't have much time for dating."

"Your plate is full."

Trisha laughed. "Yeah, my plate is full."

"I'll tell you a secret, Trisha. Your plate is always going to be full. And you're learning how to handle it. You think ahead. You make good choices. I'm proud of what you've accomplished."

"I've done some dumb things."

"Who hasn't? But I bet you learned from your mistakes."

"I guess I did. I try not to make the same mistakes."

"You're still growing, but you're on track. I just want you to know I'll always be there for you."

"Thanks, Aunt Maria."

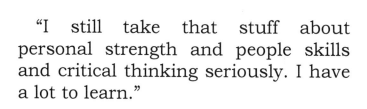

"I still take that stuff about personal strength and people skills and critical thinking seriously. I have a lot to learn."

The Gruene Hall Gig

Aunt Maria Says

If you've read this far, then you know that Aunt Maria is the kind of woman who tells it like it is. Of course, there's more to a relationship than can be told in a book like this. A lot more would have happened and a lot more would have been said. Here's a sample of the kind of things Aunt Maria would tell Trisha from time to time...

About learning...

As a teenager, your mission in life is to prepare yourself to be an adult. You only have about ten or twelve years to do this, so take it seriously. Try to have fun along the way, but remember—you won't get a second chance.

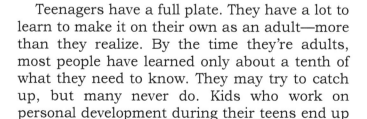

Teenagers have a full plate. They have a lot to learn to make it on their own as an adult—more than they realize. By the time they're adults, most people have learned only about a tenth of what they need to know. They may try to catch up, but many never do. Kids who work on personal development during their teens end up with an amazing edge.

Here's what teens need to work on—personal strength, people skills, critical thinking skills, life skills, and formal education. Not to mention health and fitness and service and spirituality. That's a full plate. Later, as adults, they'll need to learn about the business they're in. But success as an adult depends on how strong you are in all these areas.

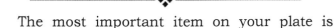

The most important item on your plate is exercising personal strength. Work on being a stronger version of the good person you already are.

Another huge item on your plate is critical thinking skills. You need to exercise judgment to control your impulses and to create a foundation for thinking logically. The window for building this foundation opens at puberty and closes in your early twenties. It's a use it or lose it deal, with enormous consequences.

One of the best ways to get smarter is to learn from other smart people. Do more asking than arguing. More listening than talking.

No teenager should be bored. Most of the stuff that will build you up and make you strong is fun and exciting. If you're bored, you've lost your way and you're in trouble.

It's great to find something you really care about. Maybe it's a sport. Or your church. Or something like music, a hobby or an extracurricular activity. Whatever it is, do it with passion. Do more of it. Get real good at it. Become a leader in it.

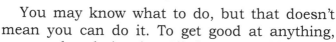

You may know what to do, but that doesn't mean you can do it. To get good at anything, you need to do it a lot. All those repetitions will wire your brain.

Just because something happened to you, it doesn't mean you learned anything from it. If you want the lesson, you have to dig for it. Ask yourself what happened, why did it happen, what were the consequences, and what would you do differently in a similar situation.

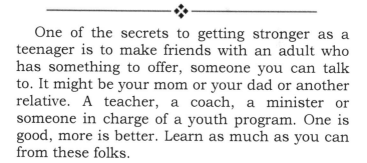

One of the secrets to getting stronger as a teenager is to make friends with an adult who has something to offer, someone you can talk to. It might be your mom or your dad or another relative. A teacher, a coach, a minister or someone in charge of a youth program. One is good, more is better. Learn as much as you can from these folks.

When thinking about a future career, remember that hard work isn't as hard if you love doing it. One of the secrets of life is to find that kind of work and do more of it. It's almost impossible to do anything really well if you don't love doing it.

If you want to get ahead, never stop learning. Work on what you know, what you can do, who you are.

---- ❖ ----

About boys...

Some guys are so cute they make your heart beat faster. This is natural, and girls like to compare notes about who's hot and who's not. But don't be fooled. When you get to know a boy, you'll start to see him differently. After the first impression, it's stuff like intelligence and strong character that make a guy seem appealing. Who he is as a person trumps good looks every time.

---- ❖ ----

Yes, sex is a great thing. But it's also complicated and potentially dangerous, not something you want to fool around with. You need more time to learn about yourself, relationships and men. You need to be ready to handle the risks, responsibilities and the commitment. If you're smart, you'll wait until you're an adult.

---- ❖ ----

Teen boys have ten times as much testosterone coursing through their bodies as girls do. They think about sex more than girls, and they want it more. They confuse sex with love. So you—not the boy—have to be the one to draw the line and tell him in a nice way.

---- ❖ ----

About friends...

Some kids think it's uncool to be serious and smart. Their idea of coolness is to joke and laugh about everything and fool around a lot. They won't find out until later how wrong they were.

———————————❖———————————

When your friends invite you to do something exciting with them, before you go along, think about the consequences. Is this something you'd like your mom or dad to watch you do?

———————————❖———————————

The people who treat you badly aren't your friends. If they put you down or say things about you behind your back, they aren't your friends. If this happens to you, find yourself some new friends.

———————————❖———————————

About alcohol, drugs, etc...

Some kids think it's fun to use alcohol and drugs. They think getting high and taking risks makes them seem adult. The truth is, these substances impair your judgment at a time when the judgment part of your brain is under construction and vulnerable. Alcohol and drugs can also do permanent damage—limit the growth of that part of your brain. And oh yeah, they're addictive.

———————————❖———————————

Smoking isn't cool, either. Get real. It's just an addiction, an expensive one that can lead to cancer and heart disease. What's so cool about that?

--- ❖ ---

About parents...

Most teenagers are disappointed when they find out their parents aren't perfect. Well guess what. Nobody has perfect parents. Nobody. So unless your parents are cruel to you, play the cards you were dealt. You don't get to choose your parents, but you do get to choose what kind of a daughter you'll be.

--- ❖ ---

Teens resent their parents, because parents aren't always sure how to give their kids the freedom and independence they crave. The trick is to keep your composure and make an effort to communicate with them. By your actions, prove to your parents you're responsible and dependable and trustworthy. Earn your freedom one step at a time.

--- ❖ ---

Some teens have parents who give them anything they want—gadgets, clothes, money, even a new car. It's a mistake to envy them. They're being robbed of the chance to learn about responsibility, hard work and striving to overcome challenges—the stuff you need to get stronger. When these kids get to be adults, they may have a hard time being independent and meeting the challenges of life.

--- ❖ ---

About self-worth...

Many of your friends will want you to be like them. To like what they like, and do what they do. But if you want to be unique and special, you have to be yourself.

❖

What does it mean to be a woman? It means to be strong in who you are—your character. It means doing the hard thing, the right thing, instead of taking the easy way out.

❖

When you make a mistake, you may feel like beating yourself up about it. Let these feelings go as quickly as you can, and then learn from what happened. Mistakes can make you smarter.

❖

People want to be nice to nice people. So if you want people to like you, treat everyone with respect, kindness and consideration.

❖

A busy life is good, but treat yourself to regular quiet time. Listen to your innermost thoughts, feelings and ideas. You're a smart person, and your brain has a lot it can tell you.

❖

Aunt Maria Says

Why Aunt Maria Talks So Much about the Teen Brain — A Brief Technical Explanation

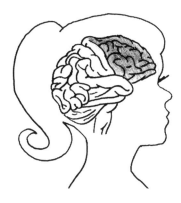

Located behind the forehead, the prefrontal cortex relates perceptions and facts to create meaning. It links cause and effect, so you can foresee future consequences. It's the seat of both creative and logical judgment, as well as both intuitive and rational problem solving. It analyzes, decides, plans, and manages, so a person isn't driven by emotional impulses. Important stuff!

The window for development of the rational decision-making part of the brain opens at puberty and closes ten to twelve years later. "Only the brain cells that fire together will wire together," as brain scientists say. It's also "use it or lose it." The unwired connections will die off, limiting the foundation for intellectual capacity for the rest of adult life. And using critical thinking can help teens stay out of trouble. But because this area is "under construction" during adolescence, it's hard for teens to use it, which accounts for their sometimes impulsive, emotional and risk-taking behavior. Bottom line—teens need to exercise this part of the brain. And because that will be hard for them, adult coaching is crucial.

Personal Strengths

Personal strengths are at the core of who a person is—doing the hard things to deal with adversity and achieve success in life, relationships and work. They're life habits developed over the years through continuous repetition.

One of the smartest things a teen can do is get involved in personal development. A variety of exercises with rich content about personal strengths are available in *ProStar Coach*, an online virtual coaching system for parents and teens developed by the author, Dr. Dennis Coates.

- Acceptance
- Accountability
- Awareness
- Commitment
- Compassion
- Composure
- Cooperation
- Courage
- Creativity
- Decisiveness
- Effort
- Empowerment
- Excellence
- Fairness
- Flexibility
- Focus
- Gratitude
- Honesty
- Initiative
- Integrity
- Intuition
- Loyalty
- Open-mindedness
- Optimism
- Passion
- Patience
- Perseverance
- Proactivity
- Rationality
- Responsibility
- Self-awareness
- Self-confidence

- Self-development
- Self-discipline
- Self-esteem
- Service
- Thoroughness
- Tolerance
- Trust
- Vision

People Skills

People skills are best practices for effective person-to-person communication. Because learning these skills is almost never addressed in high school or college, people learn how to deal with each other in a haphazard way. Hence, ineffective ways of dealing with people often cause problems in life and work relationships.

There are dozens of people skills and a proven, effective way to use each of them. Learning some of these basic skills during the teen years not only helps young people form successful relationships with friends, parents, and other adults, it prevents having to unlearn and relearn these skills later in adult life.

Here is a starter set of basic people skills for teens.

- Listening
- Giving praise
- Giving constructive feedback
- Accepting feedback
- Resolving interpersonal conflicts
- Engaging in dialogue
- Giving encouragement

This is also a good starter set for parents who haven't had people skills training. How-to videos for these communication skills and more than a dozen others are available in *ProStar Coach*, the online virtual coaching system for teens developed by the author, Dr. Dennis Coates.

More Resources for Teens

After Conversations with the Wise Aunt, read this next:

Sean Covey, *The 6 Most Important Decisions You'll Ever Make* (2004). Covey's colorful presentation and light-hearted, conversational style is perfect for teens, and his advice is consistently on target. It contains an abundance of stories from real life and anecdotes from teens. I also recommend his book, *The 7 Habits of Highly Effective Teens* (1998).

Other excellent resources:

- Michael F. Roizen, MD, and others, *You, The Owner's Manual for Teens: A Guide to a Healthy Body and Happy Life* (2011). A virtual encyclopedia of advice from a panel of doctors.
- Pamela Espeland, *Life Lists for Teens: Tips, Steps, Hints and How-tos for Growing Up, Getting Along, Learning and Having Fun* (2003). Dozens of how-tos and tips in the form of lists.
- Chad Foster, *Teenagers Preparing for the Real World* (1999). Straightforward success advice based on personal experience.
- Roger Leslie, *Success Express for Teens: 50 Activities That Will Change Your Life*

2004). Personal development exercises for teens.

- *ProStar Coach* (www.prostarcoach.com). An online virtual coaching service for developing personal strengths and people skills.

A Resource for Adults

Embedded in **Conversations with the Wise Aunt** are insights that can make a huge difference in one's life. An excellent way to make sure they are considered and related to a young person's life, the book may be read one chapter at a time, followed by a discussion with an adult after each chapter. The adult could be a parent, instructor, counselor, coach or other mentor.

To help the adult lead the discussions, Dr. Coates has created a resource called **Learning from the Wise Aunt**. It features discussion guides for each chapter of the book, including discussion questions and main points. The resource also includes worksheets for the teen. The book is available in PDF format to make it easy to print the discussion guides and reader worksheets.

Learning from the Wise Aunt is available as a FREE download at
http://www.wiseauntwiseuncle.com.

Acknowledgements

We'd like to thank Denny's old friend, Jack Pryor, whose stories about his teen years inspired us to write this book. We owe an equal debt of thanks to many other people (you know who you are) who took the time to share their teen journey stories.

This book probably wouldn't have been written if Denny hadn't been encouraged by his business partners to work on it.

We've been greatly influenced by suggestions from Meredith Bell, Debbie Pryor, Cliff Moses, Teller Coates, Patrick Barrett, Cory Richardson-Lauve, Jane Webb, Karen Scherrer and Paula Schlauch. Paula also worked out the production details of the first version of the book.

In addition, throughout the writing we've been inspired by the work of:

- Dr. David Walsh, who more than anyone we know has described the significance of teen brain development and translated this knowledge into advice for parents.
- Dr. John Rosemond's reality-based approach to parenting teens.
- Dr. Kenneth Blanchard, whose popular books about management assured me that this kind of brief, story-based approach can have a profound impact.
- Sean Covey's outstanding books for teens.

About the Authors

Dr. Dennis Coates has been CEO of Performance Support Systems, Inc., since 1987. In 1988 he developed *MindFrames*, a personality assessment based on cognitive neuroscience. In 1994 he created *20/20 Insight*, an online multi-source behavior feedback system, used by millions of people worldwide. He is also the creator of *ProStar Coach*, an online virtual coaching service for developing personal strengths and people skills. He writes about learning, personal development and parenting teens. His website: www.howtoraiseateenager.com.

Kathleen Scott retired from a career in banking to become a free-lance travel writer and is currently writing a mystery novel. She is the oldest of three sisters and has mentored her nieces and other young women. Her passions include writing, photography, gardening, cooking, and SCUBA diving. She and her husband, Denny Coates, live in the Texas Hill Country.

ProStar Coach was created for success-oriented young adults, managers, entrepreneurs and other high-performing people. Because of its rich content in the area of personal strengths and people skills, along with its emphasis on engaging critical thinking in learning exercises and changing behavior patterns, it's an outstanding personal development tool for teens. To find out more about *ProStar Coach*, go to www.prostarcoach.com.

.

Made in the USA
Lexington, KY
15 August 2013